A Book of Beetles

A Book of
BEETLES

Illustrations by
VLADIMÍR BOHÁČ

Text by
Dr JOSEF R. WINKLER

SPRING BOOKS

Graphic design by Valdemar Ungerman

Translated by Olga Kuthanová

Designed and produced by Artia for

Spring Books

Westbook House • Fulham Broadway • London

© Artia 1964

Printed in Czechoslovakia by Svoboda, Prague

First published 1964

Second impression 1965

S 1759

CONTENTS

Introduction

The modern science of insects — entomology — fills row upon row of books and scientific journals, ranging from rare, pre-Linnaean treatises to publications printed as recently as a month ago. The problem here is what to select from this vast storehouse of knowledge and how best to present that which is selected.

Beetles are not only an important order of insects confronting the scientists with innumerable unsolved problems, nor are they merely dangerous pests threatening man's economy with great financial losses. They are frequently his allies in the struggle to achieve a harvest and, if he takes the trouble to look closely, are often creatures of unexpected beauty.

Prosaic scientific treatises cannot do justice to the colour and form of these living jewels. To portray them an artist must use all the colours of his palette and even then will require more than ordinary skill to reproduce the metallic shimmer seen in some of the tropical chafers. Neither can they record the delight of a collector who discovers the rare species which has eluded him for so long, nor the excitement of the scientist who sees the solution to a problem upon which he has been labouring for months.

What follows is only a small fragment of the vast range of shapes and colours exhibited by beetles; no more than a glance at the seemingly boundless treasure house of the living world.

A few pictures will tell us more than words. Dating from different periods they seemingly have nothing in common. One of them shows a straight-backed, white-haired old man sitting with a plumb-line in his hand and watching children chasing butterflies. A gold statue of Ops, Goddess of Life, stands on a pedestal inscribed with a quotation from Pliny. It is guarded by two fallow deer wearing collars. A graceful young woman holding a book and palm leaf in her left hand raises her right to the sun. A group of three children, however, pay no heed to the others' stiff dignity. Two of them offer each other a bowl full of trapped insects. It looks like a dark day for the butterflies; nearby lies a box which contains other specimens. The third child is trying to catch water insects; placed on the bank are large vessels to hold the victims.

The other picture from the same period depicts a floral scene with large, brightly coloured blossoms offering a haven to beetles, grasshoppers, flies and other insects. Taking a slow and dignified stroll on the ground are a stag-beetle and a longicorn, while a dragon-fly hovers above a blossom. The picturesque setting is made complete by a diving beetle breaking the water's surface near the edge of the lake. Land, air and water are full of varicoloured insects which fly down or wander in to fill this romantic period engraving with shimmering effervescence.

This is the frontispiece of a beautiful book on insects, published in the eighteenth century by a famous painter of miniatures, Linnaeus' contemporary and precursor.

The above mentioned pictures are the author's only concession to the fashion of his day. The remainder of the book deals exclusively with insects as such without any superfluous embellishments. The illuminated copper engravings depict beetles and other insects so superbly and realistically that they are the object of amazement and admiration to this day. It is impossible to examine them casually and without interest, and it is difficult to decide whether their author was a greater artist than naturalist.

The next picture is more commonplace as regards style, but no less interesting as to content. It is taken from a book on ancient Egypt. The illustration depicts the sacred beetle of the ancient Egyptians carved on a precious stone — the scarab, fervidly worshipped by common folk and Pharaohs alike. It could not have been otherwise. The scarab's unusual behaviour in providing for its progeny could not pass unnoticed. The scarab was held to represent life itself! In the hieroglyphic inscriptions it is designated by the syllable *kheperi* meaning 'to be', 'exist'. The grooves were made on its back by lunar force, equalling the number of days and nights of the Moon's cycle. The scarab was believed to be of a single sex, parthenogenetic, full of natural creative force controlled by the Sun and the Moon. It could not resist the lunar force which told it when to lay its eggs and these were subject to the life-giving force of the Sun's rays which regulated the hatching of the larvae. The scarab's connection with the heavenly bodies was clearly manifest: its head was covered with a large, semicircular, crenated headshield — symbolising the Sun's rays. The scarab is an earth dweller, but the Sun marked it as its messenger. So striking and mystically marked a creature inspired worship. And so it was worshipped not only in the land of the pyramids but by all ancient civilisations. The Greeks called it *Kantharos* or *Heliokantharos*, the Romans *Scarabaeus*. Its cult was widespread. The scarab's image, sometimes a stylised version and at other times an exact likeness, was carved on precious and semi-precious stones. These minute sculptures were worn by the ancient Egyptians as amulets and had a religious phrase engraved in hieryglyphics on their flat side.

The last picture, which is the exact opposite of the foregoing ones, is so modern that we see nothing unusual in it. It shows an aeroplane with a long, misty tail streaming out behind it, and is taken from the advertising pamphlet of a firm manufacturing chemical insecticides. The plane is spraying infested fields. Pictured on the reverse side is the tin in which the product is packaged. It is doubtless brightly coloured, and stamped on its side is the image of a large beetle eminently suited for advertising purposes; its huge, protruding eyes gaze greedily at the ripe, juicy ears of corn. Nearby, however, a small cloud of the advertised product drifts down and a host of other, identical beetles flee in terror, stumble and fall, all desire for the ripe grain gone. Fear and the urge to escape annihilation are mirrored in their eyes which only a short while before were bright with greedy anticipation. The picture shows the clever packaging of the product as well as its use in spraying large, infested areas with the aid of an aeroplane.

What a vast ideological gap there is between these pictures. But could it be otherwise? Their content mirrors the long road which man's thinking has travelled over a period of thousands of years. At its beginning we have the scarab, the living reminder of the laborious building of colossal statues, the wretchedness of slaves, the pomp and glory of Pharaohs and the sublime brow of the god Ptah, which was the scarab's holy throne. And at its end we find a gleaming aeroplane helping to preserve the food supply of modern man.

This reference to the ancient Egyptians is not merely an interesting side issue but has a direct bearing on the subject. In the history of entomology the Sacred Scarab *(Scarabaeus sacer)* was probably the first beetle to be studied in the true sense of the word. It is not surprising that a beetle which had such great religious significance was studied so thoroughly by the priests who were the most cultured class of contemporary society. The scarab's fascinating mode of life was examined in detail. Egyptian artists were also the first to portray beetles, and three dimensionally at that. It is almost unbelievable that mankind had to wait a full thousand years before it acquired knowledge about other species of beetles.

The height of classical knowledge of beetles was reached by the great philosopher Aristotle. In his endeavour to set down and study everything there was to know, this Greek scholar wrote an amazing, polyhistorical work in which he devoted much attention to nature. Many of his observations which were considered figments of his imagination remained uncorroborated till modern times. In his astounding work, *Historia animalium,* he presented facts which he was the first to discover: for example, that insects copulate. He asserted that every insect is first of all a 'worm', then a pupa and finally a 'flying clear-cut image'. (To this day *imago* is the term used by scientists to designate the adult insect.) This work contains not only many correct observations but numerous errors and superstitions as well. Thus Aristotle believed that insects sprang from dead matter. According to him the Meloid beetle, which he calls *Kantharos,* emerged from the fig-tree, whereas other beetles originated from dry excrement (this opinion was apparently prompted by observation of the scarab). The errors in this work are quite understandable and are insignificant amidst the wealth of valuable knowledge contained therein. The most valuable aspect of Aristotle's work is his 'system', for he was the first person to attempt a classification of the animal kingdom. This was the first time beetles were classified as an independent group under the name of *Coleoptera,* which has remained the scientific term for that order to this day. The basis of this system, as well as the names of some of the beetle genera, latinised and incorporated by Linnaeus centuries later, remains valid to this day. That is why the Stagirite Aristotle is rightfully called the 'father of zoology'.

Aristotle is not the only outstanding naturalist of classical times: another was the Roman, Caius Plinius Secundus. His work fills thirty-seven volumes and brought him fame as the greatest naturalist of Imperial Rome. Although not of the stature of Aristotle, his fame was great, and later naturalists made frequent use of quotations from his work, see e.g. the eighteenth century engraving referred to at the beginning of this book.

Following Aristotle and Pliny there is an interval lasting several centuries. The history of natural sciences, in contrast to the history of human society, has this one interesting feature — it contains a vast gap in the process of accumulating knowledge. Throughout the entire Middle Ages Aristotle and Pliny were the only authorities on the subject and everything they wrote, both right and wrong, was accepted without question. The only person of this period who stands out as exception is Albertus Magnus (1193—1280). He, too, devoted attention to beetles and arranged them systematically.

A marked change occurs with the beginning of the Renaissance. The fifteenth century was an era of ocean voyages and curiosity in the natural phenomena of distant lands. It saw the rapid rebirth of interest in natural sciences. The invention of printing (1446) and Columbus' successful voyage to the New World (1492) mark the beginning of the new era — the Modern Age. All this had a great influence on the thinking of the educated people of the time. One of these was the Englishman Edward Wotton (1499—1555), court physician to Henry VII and a zoologist. His critical revision of Aristotle's work was the first modern attempt at scientific classification as is evident from its title *On the Differences of Animals [De differentiis animalium, libr. X.]* This work was what Renaissance man, eager to acquire knowledge of the world, had been waiting for and it inspired others.

It was not merely scientists, philosophers and doctors who were caught up in the trend initiated by Wotton, but painters and copper engravers as well. At that time there were almost no illustrations of insects in existence, and the only works of art depicting beetles were the ancient Egyptian cameos with the sacred scarab. Natural sciences at the beginning of the Modern Age was forced to look to the classical period for the foundations on which to build its edifice, since there was no legacy from the Middle Ages.

Painters and engravers deserve great credit for the growth of entomological knowledge at a time when a universally valid nomenclature had not yet been found for the members of the animal kingdom. Their pictures were the basis of morphology and anatomy and thus, in fact, the beginning of actual classification.

If the wealth of classical knowledge in the person of Aristotle belongs to the Greeks, the first torch which illuminated the centuries-long darkness and lighted the way to further knowledge of the animal kingdom was held aloft by the Englishman Wotton. The Czechs also rank high in this first phase of insect morphology thanks to Václav Hollar. In 1646 he published in Antwerp a beautiful book called *Various pictures of winged insects, worms, etc. drawn from nature by Václav Hollar, Bohemian [Diversae Insectorum aligerorum Vermiumque etc. figurae ad*

Naturam delineatae a Wenceslao Hollar, Bohemo).   Hollar's interest in this subject doubtless began in the shop of the famous engraver Matthew Merian, where he worked for a time.   This is supported by the fact that Maria Sibyl, Merian's daughter and later Hollar's mother-in-law, journeyed all the way to Surinam to view the beauty of tropical insects and published a pictorial work on the insects of that region.   She thus acquired the honour of being the only outstanding woman in the history of pre-Linnaean entomology.

Among painters in the second half of the seventeenth century the Dutchman J. Goedaert, who provided the first volume of his work on the observations of insect metamorphoses, with beautiful illuminated copper engravings, deserves the greatest credit.

The invention of the microscope at the beginning of the seventeenth century had a revolutionary effect.   Using it, the Italian scholar F. Redi, especially in his thesis, *All animals descend from animal parents (Omnia animalia per animalia parentes)*, destroyed Aristotle's erroneous ideas about the spontaneous origin of insects from dead matter.   Just as important was the research of his countryman Marcello Malpighi, who was the first to produce a complete anatomy of the insect.   Martin Lister also contributed towards proving the falsehood of the Aristotelian *generatio aequivoca;*   a treatise on beetles was published by him in London in the year 1710.

The works of painters and philosophers, as well as the microscopic technique which was being used to an ever increasing extent at that time, had a strong influence on the great but unhappy Dutch doctor and scientist, J. Swammerdam (1637—1680).   His father, a wealthy pharmacist, sent him to study medicine for he wanted his son to become a famous physician.   However, his ambition was never fulfilled.   Swammerdam paid little heed to practical medicine and spent his time in the peace of his study elaborating new and further objections to the theory of parthenogenesis and describing and explaining the shape and function of numerous internal organs.   With the aid of delicate and ingenious instruments constructed by himself he separated the individual segments of the insect and examined them under the microscope.   It is he who was responsible for precisely defining metamorphosis as opposed to the shedding of the larva's skin *(ecdysis)*.   Swammerdam was a most prominent figure in the pre-Linnaean period of entomology and we owe much to him.   However, no thanks or recognition were bestowed on him during his lifetime;   infuriated, his father, who had wanted his son to become a doctor, disinherited him.   Swammerdam died in poverty and his famous *Bible of Nature (Biblia naturae)* was not published till fifty years after his death.

Let us now turn back to the beginning of this book, to the pictures in which the children are chasing butterflies and dashing gaily around the golden statue of the goddess Ops. These charming scenes, which so excellently mirror the spirit of the time, introduce the reader to the work of the German entomologist and painter of miniatures, August Johann Roesel von Rosenhof. Called *Monthly Entertainments with Insects (Monatliche Insektenbelustigungen)* its first instalment was published in Nuremberg in 1741. The second volume of this four-volume work is devoted to beetles. Not only does it have magnificent copper engravings by the author himself, but an excellent text as well. Roesel did not deny that his art was the source of his livelihood and frequently apologised for the late delivery of the separate individual parts because of other necessary 'transactions'. The publishing of such a work was doubtless very costly in his day and the individual parts were probably quite expensive. Despite this Roesel was a truly industrious and ardent entomologist. Although it meant a smaller income he always gave precedence to quality. He strongly censured those of his customers who urged him to print only brightly coloured, attractive insects, especially butterflies. The *Monthly Entertainments* contain widely varied original observations on the life of beetles as well as Roesel's own system of classification. He presents numerous morphological details, makes drawings of dissected beetles and sings the praises of the magnifying glass; he is enthusiastic over the works of his predecessors but points out many of the inaccuracies they contain.

Roesel's importance lies primarily in his historical significance. His work was published during the lifetime of his great contemporary Carolus Linnaeus. However, it still belonged to the pre-Linnaean era; it did not make use of Linnaean nomenclature — that is subsequently incorporated into his work on the basis of the fifth edition of Linnaeus' treatise *Systema naturae*. It was not till 1758, when the tenth edition of that work was published, that we can speak of the beginning of the era of Linnaean entomology.

Since the species described by Linnaeus were not accompanied by pictures, Roesel's work can, in a sense, be considered as illustrating the *Systema naturae* even though *Monthly Entertainments* chronologically preceded Linnaeus' treatise.

This brings us to the close of the fascinating pre-Linnaean period. It began with the sacred scarab, spanned the vast void of the Middle Ages and ended with Roesel's superb *Monthly Entertainments* which fully merited the songs of praise composed by his admirers according to the custom of the day.

From Linnaeus to the Present Day

The foundations for a completely new era in the development of entomology were laid by Carl Linné (Carolus Linnaeus). It is not commonly known that his initial 'L'., which one often finds appended to the names of species described by him, would not be there if it were not for the custom, common in his day, of latinising people's names. Linnaeus' ancestral name was Ingemarsson. The Ingemarsson family, however, changed its name to 'Lindelius' after the linden tree which is said to have stood on the family estate. It was not till later that Lindelius became Linnaeus, due probably to incorrect copying of the name from the parish register. Born in 1707 as the son of a poor clergyman in the village of Rashult in the Swedish province of Smaland, it is said that he was not an exceptionally outstanding youngster. His marks at school were far from good and at one time it even seemed that young Carl might end up as a shoemaker's apprentice. Rothman, a physician who visited the family frequently, perceived the boy's talent and succeeded in persuading his parents to allow him to continue his studies. He was expected to become a clergyman like his father, but he became fascinated by nature and therefore decided to take up medicine, which at that time included the study of natural sciences.

He studied in Holland, was later appointed professor at the university of Uppsala, and was raised to the ranks of the nobility with the title of Knight of the North Star. He died in 1778 at the age of seventy-one, a man held in high esteem, respected by all and showered with honours and titles.

What is it that makes Linnaeus' work so important? Why do we divide entomology into the 'pre-Linnaean' and 'Linnaean' periods? Why do we call Carl Linnaeus the 'father of systematics' when the idea of classifying living things according to a certain order, or system, had already been set forth in classical times by Aristotle?

Linnaeus made famous an amazingly simple idea: the designation of every living thing by means of two names — according to genus and species. Thus was laid the foundation for a modern and very expedient system. The acceptance of Linnaeus' principles of nomenclature did away with the former lengthy descriptive phrases which were not only insufficiently explicit but impossible to catalogue.

Binominal nomenclature, i.e. name of genus and species, is not a brief two-word description of an animal, but a name or symbol which provides the clue to all that is known of the animal to which it is applied. Binominal nomenclature consists of the Latin or latinised names and is determined on the basis of certain definite rules. Its great advantage lies in the fact that it is internationally valid, has the same meaning for experts of all nationalities, and using it, a layman can obtain the information he requires from special literature such as catalogues, handbooks, monographs, etc.

Linnaeus' era is therefore sometimes called the 'age of systematics' or else the 'age of nomenclature'. Besides the principle of binominal nomenclature Linnaeus' other great contribution to science was his introduction of a wider range of systematic characters. He started with the wings and wing venation, but later added several other characters such as the shape of the mouthparts, antennae, etc.

Linnaeus considered beetles *(Coleoptera)* a separate, independent order. However, even he made mistakes, for he classed the cockroach *(Blatta)* and the cricket *(Gryllus)* as beetles.

His main work was the *Systema naturae* — the abbreviated form of the original title. Of the numerous editions it is the tenth, published in 1758, which is the most important. This edition was later designated and universally accepted as the basis for deciding all nomenclatural disputes, and the names of all animals described before the year 1758 were proclaimed invalid.

Linnaeus' *Systema naturae* also gave rise to the concept of the species. In previous systems 'species' and 'genus' were practically identical. It was Linné who first discovered that systematic units (categories or taxons) are of various levels. The basic unit is the *species;* one or more species form a *genus;* one or more genera form an *order*, (the term 'family' was not incorporated till later); orders form a *class*. And the classes go to make up the highest taxon — the *kingdom;* in this case the Animal Kingdom *(Regnum Animalia)*.

A concrete example will aid in explaining the basic rules of nomenclature and classification. The checkered beetle of Central Europe, interesting to forest entomologists as it is very useful in destroying bark beetles, is known by the scientific name of *Thanasimus formicarius* (L.). The generic name is *Thanasimus* (written with a capital as is the case in all generic names); *formicarius* is the specific name (always written with a small letter even when it is taken from the name of a person, e.g. the *dollmani* after the entomologist Dollman). The letter L. stands for Linné, who made the first scientific description.

When a species is transferred from one genus to another the name, or initial, of the person who first named it (i.e. the author) is written in parentheses as we see in the example. The genus *Thanasimus* Latreille does not contain only the one species *Thanasimus formicarius* but a total of almost forty species. In catalogues and other literature one can find any of these species by looking under the generic name.

To avoid confusion, only one species in a genus may bear a particular name and any species in a genus must be referred to by one name alone. If two species in a genus bear the same name, the names are homonyms and the law of priority decrees that the species to which the name was first applied must have that name and the later use of the same name for another species is forbidden. In such a case the second species must be given a new name.

If, in the course of time, a species in a genus is described more than once and is given different names each time, the law of priority states that only the oldest, correctly formed name is to be used, the later ones being suppressed as synonyms. These synonyms must never be used again in the same genus, even for another species, for this too would lead to confusion.

In the case of generic names the same rule of priority applies, but here the application is much wider, for a particular genus name may be attached to one genus only in the whole animal kingdom. Such a provision is designed to prevent, say, a worm, a beetle and a fish all being known by the same name. At first sight this may seem to be no disadvantage, but if indices and catalogues are taken into account, particularly in different languages, the dangers become obvious at once.

An example of homonymy occurs in the naming of a relative of the checkered beetle. *Thanasimus pectoralis* (Fuss), described in 1863, occurs in central Europe. In 1907 Schenkling described a different species from Rhodesia but called it *Thanasimus pectoralis*. He thus created a homonym which had to be replaced.

In 1962 Schenkling's species was renamed *Thanasimus renominatus* by J. R. Winkler. This shows how a species name need not describe a feature of the animal to which it applies. Here it merely means 'renamed'.

Thanasimus formicarius was quoted above as an example of binominal nomenclature. Comparatively recent work has disclosed the existence of subspecies within a species and the necessity of naming these units has given rise to trinominal nomenclature. The same example serves here. All European specimens of *Thanasimus formicarius* belong to the subspecies *Thanasimus formicarius formicarius*. In North Africa a slightly different population is found and this has been given the name *Thanasimus formicarius mascarensis* Corp. (Corporaal first described the subspecies).

There are other formal principles for the naming of higher systematic units. For example the name of a family is made by adding *-idae* to the root of the name of the typical genus — *Clerus* becomes *Cleridae*. A subfamily name is similarly formed from the typical genus, but here the ending *-inae* is used instead of *-idae*.

18

The importance of nomenclature must not be underestimated. It is the guarantee of order in our knowledge concerning the enormous number of animal species. That is why naturalists have worked out an International Code of Zoological Nomenclature which established the rules for ascertaining the correct names of all scientifically described animals and the groups of animals.

In addition to this, an 'International Commission on Zoological Nomenclature' has been set up to arbitrate in particularly involved cases of disputed nomenclature. This body acts under the authority of the International Zoological Congresses and these are the final courts of appeal.

A unified nomenclature and a system such as this was what early natural science so badly needed for its further development. Thanks to Linnaeus, the foundations were laid and scientists enabled to record new discoveries from all parts of the world clearly and appropriately.

The unique importance of Linnaeus' work, describing as it did some 2322 species out of the hundreds of thousands known today is easily overlooked until it is remembered that he was the first to set out a definite system and a practical method of naming and distinguishing between an indefinite number of kinds of animals and plants.

Each of his successors contributed greatly towards perfecting the system. One of the most important was the Frenchman Latreille, who increased the range of systematic characters used in Linnaeus' classification. Latreille's classification of beetles, except for a few minor points, is valid to this day. It is he who was responsible for the concept of the 'family' taxonomic unit which is an integral part of the modern system of classification.

All the culturally advanced countries witnessed the rise of universities and learned societies, the establishment of large museums, and the writing of comprehensive, systematic monographs. The number of authors who devoted themselves to the study of beetles is so great (it runs into the thousands) that it is impossible to cite them all.

Let us now turn to the last picture, the advertisement showing an aeroplane spraying a field infested with insect pests.

What importance does the study of beetles have in modern times? Doesn't mankind today have other needs which are more important than the development of entomology? Isn't the study of beetles too far removed from the current trends of science?

It might appear to be so, but that is not the case. Hundreds of entomological journals are being published throughout the world today, as well as numerous books on beetles. Research workers throughout the whole world subject beetles to microscopical examination. Entomology has acquired a new significance thanks to human progress; it is no longer a luxury nor the interesting pastime of intellectuals. The picture with the aeroplane reminds us that insects may be harmful pests which can cause the total destruction of a crop and must therefore be fought by the farmer. Insects are the concern not only of entomologists but of national economists and politicians as well. No advanced nation can afford to allow insects a free hand, for these creatures cause untold damage to the economy. Social progress is accompanied by an increase in the number of people for whom it is necessary to provide food. This gives rise to the need of cutting down crop losses. International statistics reveal that these are extremely high. The control of insect pests is being carried out the world over with all the means at man's disposal. Sometimes the scenes of battle are fertile fields of potatoes attacked by the Colorado beetle, at other times vast stretches of pine trees menaced by the bark beetle, or coconut plantations sweltering in the heat of the tropical sun and preyed upon by the voracious, giant weevil.

National economists frequently compile statistics on the damage caused by insect pests. However, few people stop to consider what sums are saved by useful, predatory beetles such as the ground beetles *(Carabidae)* or the ladybird beetles *(Coccinellidae)* which are the bane of the destructive greenfly and scale insects.

The present day study of insects is no longer limited to the mere discovery of new varieties as yet undescribed. It includes the study of the relations between insects and their environment and the relationships amongst insects themselves.

The glittering, silver aeroplane destroying insect pests might be taken as the symbol of the contemporary era in entomology. However, the tempo of scientific progress is causing even this to become an outmoded, discarded thing of the past.

The discovery of effective chemical insecticides, especially DDT and BHC, was a great step forward in the control of insect pests. However, further years of study revealed that they were two-edged weapons which fulfilled their intended purpose, extermination of the pest, but on the other hand killed other living things, including the useful, predatory species. It was found that in some cases the resistance of the pest to the chemical was greater than the resistance of its natural enemies and that using the insecticide actually allowed the pest to increase. The area sprayed by the plane presents an unbelievably sad picture of wasteland where all living things have been mercilessly destroyed. That is why this drastic, unselective method has in many instances been abandoned and should be used only on rare occasions in those cases where it is absolutely necessary, or where it is the lesser of two evils.

This does not mean that the trend is to abandon chemical control entirely. On the contrary. Insecticides have become an inestimably important aid to man. They are still being widely used, but it is to be hoped in such a way as to destroy only pests and not useful insects. The task of applied entomologists is to work out such procedures as provide effective protection against pests and at the same time cause the least harm to the other members of the animal kingdom.

Neither mechanical nor chemical control or insect pests can compare with biological control. Man's civilisation, whether he will or no, upsets the balance of the interrelations in animal societies. It is in his own interest that these interventions be kept to a minimum. That is why the scientific conception of the conservation of nature is steadily gaining in importance. The wholesale application of insecticides is a most serious interference with nature. Even the apparent economic gain cannot counterbalance the overall damage inflicted on the environment.

The following paragraphs deal with some of the factors (chiefly food relationships) which prevent the unfettered multiplication of insect numbers. Biological control makes planned use of these circumstances. The interrelations of the insect order are governed by certain laws, e.g. a species cannot multiply at an unimpeded rate as long as it is 'held in check' by its natural enemies (predators and parasites). Biological control concerns itself with the study of these factors. Pests which have spread to a new area frequently find no natural enemies there. The task of biological control is to 'introduce' predators to the new feeding ground. These may be either the pests' original enemies (in so far as they are capable of adapting themselves) or else other artificially cultivated predatory species. As soon as the predator finds sufficient food (i.e. the superabundant pest) it, too, begins to multiply rapidly. However, after the pest has been decimated the predator's numbers are also reduced for lack of food, giving rise to an equilibrium between the two, which is maintained by mutual control.

A classic example of this is the control of the scale insect *Icerya purchasi* in the U.S.A. by the Australian ladybird beetle *Rodolia cardinalis*, which was imported and artificially bred for this purpose. One could cite numerous other instances of the successful application of biological control. A pest's natural enemy may be a protozoan, a fungus, some other predaceous insect, or another animal.

Biological control is of great value because it is a natural, non-enforced method. It is based on the dynamics of biological equilibrium where the numerical quantities of the pest and its predator are like the two sides of a pair of scales.

Biological control requires extremely precise bionomical study and experimentation as well as the collaboration of a large number of experienced research entomologists.   Its greatest disadvantage is this elaborate and exacting research and laboratory preparation required before it can be put into practice.   Testing the effectiveness of various insecticides is a relatively simple matter, whereas the study of the food relationships between various organisms frequently presents many difficulties.   Sometimes laboratory experiments are successful, but mass breeding of the predator is difficult;   sometimes the predator proves less resistant to the climatic conditions than its host.   As one can see, the successful introduction of a suitable predator in biological control is not a simple matter; however, it is of great value because it is enduring.

All data on the food relationships of beetles are of great importance and we still know comparatively little.   One never knows if a new discovery which today is purely academic may not be applied tomorrow in practice to serve the needs of mankind.

A thorough study of the bionomics of insects makes the prognosis of their excessive multiplication possible.   This, in turn, allows the planned development of preventive control by the introduction of predators, thus avoiding the necessity of employing the harsher method of insecticides on a full-scale outbreak.

Of all the methods of protecting plants, biological control is the best and has a great future.

This is the reason why entomology has not come to a standstill but is developing with rapid strides, employing all the techniques of modern science to this end. Entomology has not decreased in importance.   On the contrary its social significance is becoming even greater and future historians may one day call this stage of its growth (which is serving mankind directly) 'the era of economic entomology'.

As Illusive as a Rainbow

The coloration of many beetles is far from dull.   In some cases the magic is created by a single colour tone, in others we find a whole, dazzling array of colours;   delicate, soft pastel shades on the one hand, hard and glittering metallic reflections on the other.

And yet most of these breathtaking, shimmering colours do not exist in reality. The magnificent metallic colours are the very ones which no chemist could extract from the body of the beetle.   They are an illusion, just like the rainbow. The surface of the beetle's body includes a complex polysaccharide called chitin, and several additional substances. In some beetles it is very thick and like a strong plate of armour, in others it is very thin, wrinkled and leathery. The body covering of every beetle consists of several layers which in turn are comprised of microscopically thin ones. These break up light into its various colour components and produce the metallic reflections in some beetles. That is why the majority of beetles, especially the ones with a bright glitter, do not change colour after they are killed. Museum collections, frequently containing specimens as much as one hundred years old, provide proof of this colour constancy. In other instances, however, we observe that certain changes do occur due to the effect of the ethyl acetate or other agent used to kill the beetles, or to the effect of light on the preserved specimens. Scarlet or vermilion coloured elytra acquire an orange or rich, red-brown tinge; fresh, leaf-green turns a dingy yellow-brown. This is often true in the case of the pastel-coloured beetles. We can be sure that the body covering of species which change colour in this way contains, in addition to structures producing colours by the refraction and interference of light, pigments of widely varied chemical properties. For example the pinkish red larvae of the Colorado beetle (*Leptinotarsa decemlineata* Say), or the deep red elytra of other leaf beetles (chrysomelids) are due to the presence of the pigments known as lipochromes or carotinoids. It is the same pigment that produces the rich red colour of tomatoes. The yellow-red colour of numerous other species is produced by a mixture of several pigments also belonging to the carotinoid group.

Other pigments to be found in the body covering of the beetle include the melanins, which produce a black colour and the ommochromes, producing a yellow-brown colour. It seems that the green coloration of beetles is produced by a great number of pigments whose chemical structure is still undetermined. The pigments may be contained in groups or layers of special cells, or in the exocuticle, or sometimes beneath the body covering altogether. Colour pigments in beetles remain a subject for future research; more attention has been devoted to the study of pigments in butterflies and especially in some coccids which are the source of excellent natural dyes.

The most beautiful colour effects in beetles are produced by combined coloration, i.e. the combination of structural colours and pigments. Frequently, as a result of light refraction, a pastel colour acquires an enamel gloss; at other times the softness of pastel hues alternates with the sheen of metallic colours.

In addition to the actual coloration, the body surface may bear numerous strikingly coloured structures which heighten the beauty of the beetle. These include various kinds of hairs, bristles, small tufts of short, close set filaments called tomentose vestiture, or brightly coloured spatulate scales. The bodies of some beetles, especially certain species of tropical Buprestids, are covered with a powdery layer somewhat like pollen or rime.

The significance of the beetle's coloration is not precisely known. No one has yet discovered why one species has a black dot whereas another, closely related species has a black marking in the form of parallel stripes, despite the fact that they both live in the same place and in roughly similar conditions.

There is no doubt that the overall coloration of beetles is closely linked with the conditions in which they live. Evidence for this are the blind, cave-dwelling (cavernicolous) beetles. These species, adapted to the darkness of their underground habitat, are either totally blind or else their eyes are almost non-existent, their pubescence is limited to single, long, sensory bristles and their bodies are pale in colour. Beetles living in darkness cannot perceive colours nor are they brightly coloured themselves. On the other hand, many beetles living on the earth's surface, especially on plants, glow with all the colours of the spectrum. Predatory beetles living on the ground beneath the plant undergrowth (particularly the ground beetles — *Carabidae*) are often black, dark brown or some other earthy colour.

Similarly, the coloration of aquatic beetles harmonises with their environment. Black, brown and olive green tones predominate, with yellow-brown occurring less frequently. They may also have distinct patterns on their elytra but these are always much less colourful than those of dry land beetles.

Coloration which only roughly corresponds to the main colours of a beetle's habitat might be termed as universally adapted. On the other hand, coloration which tries to be exactly like that of some part of its surroundings is called cryptic coloration or mimicry, the general phenomenon being known as mimesis. The purpose of mimicry is to render the beetle invisible in its natural habitat, or to cause it to be mistaken for some other animal. Many species of longicorns *(Cerambycidae)*, which live on the branches and trunks of trees, have greyish spots which are indistinguishable from the minute growths of lichen scattered over the bark of the tree. As long as the longicorn doesn't move it is almost invisible. Similar mimetic masking exists in the Cassidid family whose members live on grass roots and resemble the achenes, bracts, and other parts of plants lying on the ground. Their grass green colour disappears completely when they are killed and mounted; these species are an example of the many beetles whose coloration is produced exclusively by pigments.

The Cassidids show form mimesis which frequently occurs in conjunction with colour mimesis. Other examples are some of the leaf beetles (chrysomelids) of the family Hispidae, whose thorax and elytra are dotted with minute, sharp thorns so that they look like a prickly fruit.

One could cite many examples of mimesis, from slight camouflaging to total masking where the beetle is absolutely indistinguishable from its surroundings and is usually discovered only by chance or when it makes a slight movement.

Shapes are as Varied as Colours

Even those beetles which at first glance look quite ordinary have many interesting features when examined closely. Take the ground beetles of the genus *Carabus*, for instance. The rapacity of these beetles is unbelievable. The large but defenceless caterpillar attacked by the ground beetle is torn to shreds in the twinkling of an eye. The great entomologist J. H. Fabre rightly compared the activity of a group of ground beetles in captivity to the efficiency of a modern slaughterhouse. When we take a close look at the ground beetle we find long, strong legs ensuring the great speed and endurance necessary for exploring large areas and making surprise attacks on its prey; large, strong and sharp, scimitar-shaped mandibles; a hard, thick, chitinous armour which protects the body of the assailant. On the other hand, phytophagous beetles are equipped for a peaceful life on plants. Their legs are much shorter and the tarsal joints are short and broad. The mandibles are not like daggers but are wide and blunt. If the mandibles of predaceous beetles are used as daggers or razors, those of phytophagous beetles function more like a grinder or milling machine, their task being to cut, crush and grind leaves or other parts of plants. Whereas carnivorous species run quickly from place to place phytophagous beetles usually move at a slower pace. Their legs are not adapted for covering great distances (wings are used for this purpose), but for climbing on the plants they feed on. Particularly well equipped for this mode of life are the weevils. Their mouth-parts, located in the tip of the rostrum, not only enable them to nibble plants but also to bore into various fruits and seeds which are sometimes quite hard. Longicorns have huge mandibles but often their most difficult task is gnawing their way out of the pupal coccoon.

The adaptation of aquatic beetles is most interesting. Water beetles *(Dytisci-dae)* are shaped like a boat, being well suited for rapid movement in water. Like ground beetles, to whom they are related, these water beetles have thin, filiform antennae and large, sharp mandibles. In order to make lightning

25

attacks on their prey their hind legs are flattened and shaped like oars. With these the predaceous water beetles swim quickly and catch insect larvae, small fish or tadpoles by surprise.

Quite frequently the males of a beetle species have the front legs distinctly longer than the middle and hind pairs. These enable the male to clasp the body of the female during mating.

The anterior tibiae of beetles which dig in the ground *(Georyssidae, Heteroceridae* and some of the family *Scarabaeidae)* are fossorial in character. The crenate head-shield of the sacred scarab already mentioned serves the same purpose.

Another type of adaptation to the beetle's mode of life is flattening. *Hololepta plana* Fuessly, which lives beneath the loose bark of felled tree trunks, is so flattened that its height is only a small fraction of its width. This adaptation enables it to burrow deep under the peeling strips of bark. Examples of flattened beetles are to be found in other families as well. One of the most interesting is the species *Platypsyllus castoris* Ritsema which forms the independent family *Platypsyllidae*. This rare and interesting beetle lives on the skin of the beaver. Its appearance is so unusual that for a long time no one knew where to place it and whether it could even be classed as a beetle; this case, of course, is an exception. Beetles, except in certain rare instances, are not parasitic.

Many species living on wood have an elongate, cylindrical body; sometimes they have larvae which bore tunnels in the timber, sometimes they enter tunnels made by other insects which they find and eat.

Simple observation demonstrates that predatory beetles usually have more prominent eyes than those feeding on plants, and that beetles living in perpetually dark habitats have small eyes or are completely eyeless.

All the above adaptations, as well as many others too numerous to be listed here due to the limited extent of this book, are important to the survival of the beetle, particularly as regards the procuring of food. In addition to these some beetles have special form adaptations which influence sexual selection.

Sexual selection, as proved by Charles Darwin, enables the fittest to by the most successful in the propagation of the species and to transmit this fitness to future generations. It is evidenced in the battles waged by males for the female when the less fit and weaker individuals are driven off or killed and so do not succeed in mating.

The most spectacular and menacing weapons for these jousts are displayed by the males of the stag beetles *(Lucanidae)*. Their mandibles are very large and frequently antler-like in shape.

Such peculiarities of form are to be found in vast numbers amongst beetles. Similar variation can readily be observed, for example, when comparing the antennae of different species. In some they are filiform, in others they are clubbed, serrate, pectinate, lamellate, and in some special cases they have a peculiarly irregular shape. As regards the shape and surface of the elytra, there is also vast diversity.

The wealth of varied shapes to be found amongst beetles is so great that they can only be briefly touched upon here. However, a sharp-eyed observer will himself discover many interesting peculiarities in every species. These are never an end in themselves but always serve some vital function.

What Lies Hidden Beneath the Chitinous Armour?

Let us take a closer look at the internal organs which lie beneath the beetle's body covering. Because of the hard, outer shell it is difficult to examine their shape and purpose and therefore it is necessary to say a few words about them.

The life processes of the beetle are different from those of vertebrates and man. The insect's anatomy shows that the basic life functions common to all living creatures follow a different, distinct course, peculiar to insects alone.

Take respiration, for instance. Beetles do not breathe through the mouth and have no lungs where blood can be oxygenated by a chemical process, that is by the combining of oxygen with a chemically active colouring matter such as haemoglobin. The mouth of the insect has nothing to do with respiration; this is accomplished by the tracheal system. The tracheae are thin tubes which receive air by means of special, circular apertures called airholes, stigmata or spiracles. These can be clearly seen on the side of the abdomen as round dots, which are usually of a lighter shade. Leading from the spiracles to the inside of the beetle's body is a complex system of tracheae which branch into a myriad of fine tubules. Some beetles that are particularly active and consume great quantities of oxygen also have special air-storage pockets called tracheal air sacs. The thinnest air tubes, known as the tracheoles, bring air to the individual cells or cell groups. It can be seen that there is a fundamental difference between the respiration of insects and that of vertebrates. In insects the blood is an indirect carrier of oxygen which is taken up only in physical solution. In vertebrates, however, the oxygen is carried in chemical combination by respiratory pigments.

The blood of insects is usually completely colourless, but in some instance has an oily, yellowish appearance. Respiratory pigments occur in it only rarely and when they do they are freely dispersed and not contained within blood cells.

Insect blood does, however, contain cells and some of these are concerned with clotting over wounds, while others are called into play when the animal is moulting its skin.

The circulatory system is an open one. The heart is a tube running the length of the body and equipped with lateral valves. By pumping movements and by the opening and closing of these valves, the blood of an insect, which fills the body cavity and so bathes all the tissues and organs, is kept in motion and plays its part in the translocation of food and waste products.

The great vitality and activity of many beetles proves that this strange circulatory system in no way impairs their vital functions. Some experts have suggested that this type of circulatory system can adequately fill the requirements of only comparatively small organisms and give this as the reason why insects, as compared with vertebrates, never attained greater dimensions.

The size range of beetles is truly vast. For example, the tropical longicorn beetle *Titanus giganteus* of South America measures approximately 13 cm. long. On the other hand there are *Trichopterygidae*, whose members, distinguished by their beautiful featherlike wings, are among the smallest of beetles, being only a few tenths of a millimetre long.

The beetle's digestive system is also very interesting. At the hind end of the oesophagus is an enlarged crop which is followed by an interesting organ, the so-called chewing stomach or proventriculus. Food which has been shredded, sawn or cut by the mouthparts is here ground into a fine mash by sharp, chitinous, needle-like teeth, plates or leaves. It then proceeds to the next section of the alimentary canal where the actual chemical digestion takes place. For excretion, which in vertebrates is carried out by the kidneys, insects have special organs called malpighian tubes. Beetles have four or six of these. The tubes are reinforced and have muscle fibres on their outer surface. Contraction of these muscles makes the tubes pulsate. It is interesting to note that the malpighian tubes also participate in the production of silk fibres. Amongst beetles this occurs in the larvae of longicorns and weevils which before pupation produce a liquid which solidifies into silk fibres on coming into contact with the air, and is used to spin a cocoon.

The beetle's nervous system is also of considerable importance. Insects are incapable of abstract mental activity. Whereas the behaviour of some higher mammals reveals a certain amount of intelligence, e.g. memory, profit from experience, imitative ability, etc., insects have few of these traits. Their reactions are largely instinctive and this is the most characteristic feature of insect behaviour. No insect female ever teaches her offspring to catch prey, crawl, swim or fly as is true of the vertebrates. Insects 'know' all these things automatically from the very first day of their life; there is no difference between the 'uninitiated' young and their 'experienced' elders.

Insects 'know' exactly how to overpower their prey, how to conceal themselves from their enemies, how to escape them, etc. Instincts also govern the manner of courting, mating and care of the young. That insects can learn simple things has been proved in the laboratory. That some insects have the power to remember is well-known to every beekeeper, but in the main the reactions of an insect to a particular circumstance seem invariable and instinctive.

The nervous system which initiates the instinctive responses is located on the underside of the body. It consists of two longitudinal cords which extend from the rear section of the head, down the thorax and usually over the major part of the abdomen. These two cords are identical and in close proximity to each other. Placed along their length are nerve centres called ganglia. These ganglia are paired and joined together by short transverse connectives so that the nervous system often looks like a ladder. The most important ganglia are those to which the cerebral and suboesophageal glands are attached.

Extending from each ganglion are nerves which divide into nerve branches having various functions such as innervating the external sensory organs, activating the various glands, controlling the movements of muscles, etc. Movement is a vitally important factor for many beetles. It has been proved that insects have powerful muscles and that many beetles are truly 'strong men'.

At least a brief reference should be made to certain special glands and their secretions. These glands are either single or multi-celled, of varied origin, and situated in various parts of the body. Many of their secretions are attractant or repellent in function. Thus, for instance, the beetle may have a sweet-smelling scent with which to lure its mate, a drop of poison or nauseous vapour for its enemy.

Defensive secretions generally have a foul, repugnant odour and their function is to ward off enemies, even those that are much larger than the beetle itself. This character is highly developed in many beetle families, e.g. the rove beetles *(Staphylinidae)* and the ground beetles *(Carabidae)*. These beetles are capable of ejecting an evil-smelling secretion to a distance of several centimetres. This secretion can also irritate the mucous membrane and cause obstinate, unpleasant inflammations, particularly of the eye.

Science recently made an unusual discovery as regards the cosmopolitan beetle *Tribolium destructor* Uyttenb., belonging to the family *Tenebrionidae* which attack stored grain. These small, elongate, brown-black beetles exude drops of a yellow, oily fluid which has a formidable chemical effect — it cripples the beetle's own progeny. (For further details see page 112).

Fright and possibly other unpleasant sensations are suffered by the enemies of the bombardier beetle (a ground beetle of the tribe *Brachynini*) when it fires its ammunition. This beetle ejects from its anus a small cloud of vapour accompanied by an explosive sound. This ability is shared by some members of the tropical family *Paussidae* dwelling in the nests of ants and termites.

Poisonous beetles, in particular those belonging to the oil beetles *(Meloidae)*, have already been discussed in the section on warning coloration. From the Middle Ages cantharidin, obtained from the body of the *Lytta vesicatoria* (L.), has been frequently used for medicinal purposes.

Arrow poison has also been made from the bodies of beetles. Kalahari Bushmen dip their arrows in poison made from the pupae of the South African leaf-beetle *Diamphidia locusta* Boh. This poison is very violent, especially if it is introduced directly into the blood stream. Partial paralysis and blood in the urine are followed by complete paralysis and death.

Another poisonous South African leaf-beetle is *Blepharida evanida* Boh. whose secretion is probably not as virulent and has a less pronounced effect.

Aromatic secretions play a part in bringing the sexes together for mating. It seems that most species have a specific, characteristic scent occurring in one or sometimes both sexes. Human beings are insensible to most of these perfumes, but some species emit a strong, penetrating odour which is easily perceived by man. One example is *Aromia moschata* (L.), the musk beetle, which has an extremely strong smell.

Beetle odours are still a subject for further scientific study. Since a large number of these scents are not perceived by humans it is all the more difficult to ascertain their chemical properties. That is why in most cases we are unable to determine their function in the beetle's life.

Reproduction

The beetle has one more important system and that is the reproductive apparatus. The vast numbers of insects inhabiting this earth are eloquent proof of its efficiency.

Beetles are divided into males and females. As a rule the sex cannot be determined on the basis of the beetle's general appearance. In some cases, however, secondary sexual characteristics are well developed. The sexes may differ in form, this being known as sexual dimorphism, or else in colour, which is termed sexual dichroism.

The reproductive organs are activated by hormones produced by the endocrine glands.

Reproduction is almost always bisexual — the egg produced by the female must be fertilised by the male. Only in rare instances do we find examples of parthenogenesis, i.e. where there is reproduction without mating.

The female lays fertilised eggs from which the minute, first stage larvae, which are about the same size as the egg, emerge. The larvae shed their skin periodically *(ecdysis)*, each ensuing stage *(instar)* being larger and heavier. The larval phase is the only period during which an insect grows. The grub emerging from the egg is translucent and barely visible, and before it pupates has increased to many times its original size. The adult beetle, on the other hand, is a 'finished product' and can no longer grow.

Beetle larvae vary greatly in form and habit. Those of the ground beetles, rove beetles and burying beetles are slender, very active and often dark-coloured. The familiar mealworm and wireworm are the larvae of a tenebrionid and of some click beetles. The larvae of some leaf beetles are very like caterpillars, while the white grub of the gardener is the larva of the cockchafer or maybug. They are always well adapted to their environment and mode of life: predaceous larvae, feeding on the ground, have a harder and stronger body covering, the larvae of Chrysomelids, feeding on plants, have beautiful, bright colours, larvae dwelling permanently underground are yellowish or entirely white and capable of only limited movements.

The larvae of all beetles are quite unlike the adult in structure. After several moults the mature larva is ready for pupation. During this phase it undergoes a complete transformation, i.e. it must be 'put in the melting pot' and 're-cast' as a mature beetle. This 'reconstruction' takes place during the pupal stage. Insects having an incomplete metamorphosis (e.g. bed-bugs, dragon-flies, Orthopteroid insects) have no quiescent pupal stage.

The larva's life task is to eat as much food as possible and store up such reserves of energy as will suffice for the complex process of transformation into an adult beetle *(imago)* that occurs during the pupal stage. The main phase of the transformation is the complete disintegration *(histolysis)* of the pupal tissues and the creation of the separate organs of the adult beetle from this chaotic mass. The whole process is directed by hormones. Only when one stops to consider that the larva always develops into a beetle, identical with its parent down to the smallest detail, does one realise what miracle of nature the metamorphosis of insects is. Just as the task of the larva is to store energy, so the purpose of the pupa is to enable the transformation of the *larva* into the *imago*. The adult beetle, in contrast to this, exists primarily to fulfil the reproductive phase in the insect's life history.

Beetles are Everywhere

The decline of one generation and the energetic onslaught of the next is merely the replacement of old, exhausted forces by fresh, new blood.

'Be fruitful and multiply,' . . . is a command obeyed to the letter by every single species. The extent of its fulfilment, however, is influenced by a number of internal and external factors. These may be differences in climate, the limited occurrence of the plant on which a particular beetle feeds, etc. Species which feed only on one plant can exist only in those areas where the plant grows. Natural enemies such as birds, mammals, predaceous insects, fungi or moulds are also a serious factor in restricting the spread of insects. It is evident that these insects cannot multiply unhindered and that their distribution is controlled and limited by external, ecological factors.

Beetles may be found almost everywhere. As a result of their greatly diversified ways of life there seems no habitat unsuited to some species or other. There are aquatic beetles, beetles that live in the immediate proximity of water, either on the sandy or muddy banks of rivers, ponds, and lakes, and others on plants growing in water.

Different kinds of plants provide food for numerous phytophagous beetles. Some feed on the roots, others on the stems, leaves, blossoms or fruits of the plant. Those beetles which feed on wood form another group *(xylophagous)*. In some cases they eat the cambium layer (e.g. bark beetles) in others the wood itself. And even here there are differences between the wood of living trees and that of dead trees. The loose bark of felled trees is a collector's paradise.

Cultivated sites also have their own beetle fauna, more limited in variety than in wild areas where there are numerous different kinds of plants.

It is impossible to enumerate all the many types of beetle communities. Each includes not only those species which dwell there because of their food plant requirements but also the enemies (predators and parasites) of those species.

Mention must also be made of omnivorous insects which feed on decaying plants as well as animals and occasionally even attack weaker insects. Many of these beetles, especially those which feed on carrion *(cadavericolous)*, are very useful.

Some beetles live together with other insects. Many species, known as *myrmecophiles*, live in ants' nests where they are either welcome guests, tolerated visitors and sometimes even unwelcome lodgers. Others, known as *termitophiles*, live in termites' nests, and still others in bees', wasps', or hornets' nests.

Beetles are to be found in quite unexpected places. Mention has already been made of the blind, pale-coloured species which live in dark habitats. Certain specialised species, extremely modest as to their needs, are to be found even in deserts. These subsist on the roots of the sparsely growing grass. However, desert fauna is fairly limited as regards both number and variety of species. This, of course, does not apply to the green oases which simply teem with beetles.

Approximately five species of parasitic beetle are known to science. Rare and exceptional indeed, when one considers that there are almost half a million known species of *Coleoptera* in existence.

Beetles are found all over the world, the greatest number of species occurring in the tropics in the region of the equator. The farther the distance from this zone, the smaller their number. However, a few species are to be found even in the arctic regions. The tropical and subtropical regions of the Old and New World are the beetles' paradise. The study of beetles in these countries has been more or less haphazard to date. Only Europe, North America and Japan can be considered as having been studied thoroughly, and it is on the fauna of these territories that the greatest number of comprehensive works has been published. In other countries there are still vast areas which have not been investigated as yet and the beetle fauna, with the exception of large, striking and colourful species, is practically unknown. More than 600,000 species have been scientifically described to date. Experts, however, assert that many more still remain to be discovered. These are mainly the smaller sized beetles living in the tropical and subtropical regions.

Beetles, then, are everywhere. Those who wish to see them in their natural habitat need not go far in order to enjoy their beauty and observe the peculiarities of their habits.

Collecting Beetles

Anyone who is interested in beetles and wishes to know more about them cannot do much without a collection of his own. All that is generally known about collecting is that beetles are caught, immersed in alcohol and mounted on pins (while they are alive, as some people still believe). There is much more to it than this. Although gathering beetles and building up a collection is not difficult, it is nevertheless a much more complicated affair than people generally believe.

The very process of collecting is not clear to the layman. If he has a friend who collects beetles he will remember him on his Sunday outing if a beetle happens to settle on his shirt sleeve. He will examine it from all sides and suddenly discovering the magic world of beetles for himself, will put the poor creature into a matchbox, and hand it triumphantly to his friend on the following day. Usually his effort has been wasted for the box turns out to be empty, the imprisoned beetle having escaped by squeezing through a crack or nibbling a hole. At other times the beetle is still there and the finder proclaims that he's never seen 'such a queer beetle' in his life and that it is probably some unknown species, only to have it turn out to be a very common species of ground beetle, longicorn or soldier beetle. Such a person naturally ponders bitterly on his friends ingratitude. However, there have been cases when an absolutely un-initiated layman has brought such a matchbox containing an unusually rare specimen which expert collectors have been seeking vainly for years.

A true collector goes out into the countryside in quest of beetles equipped with the necessary implements. The main requirement is a jar or a sufficient number of corked, thin glass tubes containing sawdust damped with ethyl acetate. The jar must be flat if possible (so that it can be carried comfortably in a pocket), and must have thick walls and a wide neck (so that it can easily be cleaned). It is filled about half-way with sawdust which has been previously rinsed or sifted to rid it of dust. Cut strips of filter paper are sometimes used instead of sawdust. Either the one or the other is necessary in order to prevent the beetles from defiling or damaging each other.

The beetles in the jar are killed by the fumes of the ethyl acetate. Ethyl acetate has a pleasant fruity odour, evaporates quickly (on lengthier excursions it has to be replenished by the addition of a few drops), and kills beetles quickly and painlessly. Immersion in alcohol is an obsolete method which is used only when no other means of killing the insect is available. Beetles asphyxiated by ethyl acetate fumes remain relaxed whereas those immersed in alcohol become stiff, thus making their subsequent preparation more difficult.

The collector's equipment should also include entomological forceps for grasping the beetle without damaging it. If each beetle were to be caught separately the collection would be added to at a very slow rate and that is why other necessary items are a sweep net, beating tray and sieves.

At first glance the net appears to be like that used to catch butterflies, only more massive. It consists of a white cloth bag secured to a sturdy metal frame attached to a handle. The net is swept back and forth with rapid sideways strokes amidst vegetation. Every once in a while it is examined closely and the beetles caught in it are removed.

A sifter can be a simple kitchen of medium mesh, shaken over a white paper or sheet. Better results may be obtained using such a sieve with a cloth bag attached beneath it and tied at the bottom by a purse string. Leaf litter, dead bark or other debris is placed in the sieve. When the sieve is shaken, any small insects present will pass through the mesh of the sieve and may be extracted by opening the bottom of the bag over a sheet or a suitable container.

The beating tray is always quite large. It is either 'net-like' or 'umbrella-shaped'. The net used for this purpose consists of a shallow bag on a large, circular metal frame with the handle turned inward. The 'umbrella' is just like a real one as regards both size and shape and can easily be made from an ordinary umbrella by simply stretching a white cloth over the framework and shortening the handle. The beating tray is placed beneath a tree or bush which is then beaten or shaken; the insects which drop down into the tray are quickly gathered and placed in a jar or tube.

A few further important items are required for successful collecting. These include a sharp knife or small pick for loose bark, a notebook and a pencil. (Notes are never made in ink out-of-doors as possible dampness might impair their legibility.)

Another extremely useful aid which anyone can easily make by himself is the aspirator. It frequently proves far more useful than forceps. The aspirator is a hollow glass cylinder plugged by one or two bored stoppers in which short glass tubes are inserted. One of these tubes is slightly bent and its end is cut off obliquely; the end inside the cylinder is open. The inner end of the second tube is covered with a piece of muslin or some other such material and attached to the outer end is a length of rubber tubing. By sucking on the end of this tubing the air pressure is lowered inside the aspirator and strong suction is produced at the outer end of the open tube. When this is held close to a beetle the inrushing air sucks the insect into the aspirator. The muslin prevents it from being drawn into the other tube and thus into the mouth.

This is as brief as possible an account of the collector's equipment. With these few items it is possible to achieve excellent results and collect a large quantity of worthwhile specimens. One most important point has not been mentioned. The most valuable find is absolutely worthless if it is not accompanied by the following information: the locality of capture, the date of capture and the collector's name. One must never depend on one's memory. Immediately a beetle is caught it is necessary to put a slip of paper with this information into the collecting jar or tube so as to eliminate any possibility of confusion. When recording the locality its official name, i.e. the one appearing on maps, etc., should be used. If the name covers a wide area it is necessary to be more precise by recording the name of the political or postal district in which the locality is situated.

The collected specimens are preserved and mounted at home. The preparation of beetles is very simple. It consists mainly of arranging the legs and antennae, pinning or 'carding' the insect and letting it dry. However, certain points should be noted. A beetle killed with ethyl acetate should not be mounted for a few days. Then it is most relaxed and need not be moistened. If it should happen that the collecting vessel has a defective stopper, the ethyl acetate has dried up, and the specimen become stiff, there is no need for dismay. All that is necessary is to relax the beetle. This is done with the aid of a Petri dish or other similar covered vessel in which very moist conditions may be produced. The bottom of the dish should be covered with clean, washed, river sand or a layer of filter paper which is sufficiently moist and on which the beetle is carefully placed. Handling the beetle in a dry state usually results in damage to the appendages, whereas specimens which have been properly relaxed can be mounted even after several years. Beetles are left in the relaxing dish for three days at the most if only water is used. Sometimes, however, a few drops of glacial acetic acid are added to facilitate relaxing and in this case it is necessary to remove the beetles within 48 hours.

Items used for the actual mounting include forceps, fine brushes, preparation needles consisting of needles in suitable holders, and a spreading board of peat or cork. Larger beetles are pinned with correspondingly thick pins, always passed at right angles through the right elytron. The term 'pins' as used in this text always refers to special entomological pins which have very little in common with ordinary ones and can be obtained from dealers in entomological apparatus.

The legs and antennae of pinned beetles are always placed as close to the body as possible to prevent their being damaged. The correct position is achieved by arranging them on the spreading board with the aid of pins. In the case of smaller beetles which are carded, the legs are allowed to extend further sidewards as they are protected by the card.

Formerly it was customary to mount all beetles on pins. In old collections one frequently finds even minute insects impaled on extremely thin pins. Today, however, the trend is to attach beetles with adhesive to thin but stiff card whenever possible.

Cards are of several different shapes. Those most commonly used have rounded corners. The beetle is placed on its back, its legs are arranged in the desired position, and a small drop of adhesive is put on the card. Best suited for this purpose are the so-called fish glues (e.g. Seccotine) which are soluble in water and don't crack when dry as gum arabic does. Just the right amount of adhesive should be applied — neither too much nor too little. The beetle is then carefully transferred to the drop of adhesive and placed so that the underside of its thoracic segments adhere to the card. Under no circumstances should adhesive be applied to the legs or antennae. A fairly thick pin is then passed through the card whilst still on the spreading board. A pinning block (graded wooden steps), with holes of appropriate depth, is also used to ensure uniformity in height.

Each mounted beetle, whether pinned or carded, must have a data label, i.e. a cardboard label bearing pertinent data — where and when it was found as well as the collector's name. A collection without data labels is absolutely worthless from the scientific point of view (even though it may contain the rarest of specimens).

The prepared insects are kept in reserve containers until their scientific names have been ascertained, after which they are put in the appropriate drawer or box.

Cabinet drawers are an essential item of every collection. They have a soft bottom, usually made of pressed peat, into which it is easy to stick pins. The drawers should be covered inside with white paper and they should have tight-fitting lids. Series of specimens are placed in the drawers in neat columns, one species to each column. If a species is represented by only relatively few specimens a column may be sectioned to accommodate two or more species. The lids of cabinet drawers are always glazed, but boxes, which can be arranged like books on a shelf should have lids that exclude the light. It is preferable to store such boxes in a sturdy, tightly closed cupboard where they are protected from damp, light, dust and insect pests. Glass-covered containers with specimens must never be hung on walls.

Special entomological cabinets are expensive, and their drawers are seldom interchangeable from one cabinet to another. It is cheaper and usually more convenient to use entomological store-boxes which can be obtained from dealers in a variety of patterns and materials. For beetles they should not be too long, and it is most convenient if they are uniform in size.

Arranging a collection, though not an easy task by any means, is nevertheless highly rewarding. Only a well arranged collection in uniform containers can properly fulfil its function of aiding in the study of beetles as well as being a source of pleasure. In order that the collection can be arranged correctly the naturalist needs reference books, catalogues, atlases and good optical equipment, — if nothing else then at least an entomological lens which magnifies insects 20 to 30 times their original size. An excellent though costly instrument is a binocular stereoscopic microscope. With such a microscope it is possible to study the external morphology of even the smallest beetles with ease.

One thing must not be forgotten: adequate and regular disinfection of the collection, for which purpose paradichlorbenzene or nitrobenzene are very suitable. These chemicals with their typical museum-like odour evaporate (that is the reason why the collection should be kept in a tightly closed cabinet), and their fumes either destroy or drive away carpet beetles and other insects harmful to collections. It is necessary to disinfect the collection at least once a year, better still twice — in the spring and autumn. This can be done by inserting an ampoule containing the chemical in each box and by placing several larger open vessels in the cupboard so that the fumes permeate the surrounding air as well.

Well disinfected and properly maintained collections can last centuries whereas a neglected one is a sad sight to behold in quite a short time.

Every properly organised collection of beetles, even the smallest, is a scientific document. It represents a great expenditure of time and effort (aside from the pleasant memories evoked by each data label) and for that reason deserves to be maintained in good condition.

Man's interests change with time. It may so happen that a beginner's enthusiasm wanes and he loses interest in collecting insects. If such be the case it is only fair to give the collection to a natural history museum which is able to give it the necessary care.

The length of the beetles was measured from their head to the tip of the elytra.

PLATES

Cicindela chinensis DEG. *ab. japonica* THUNB.

Family *Cicindelidae*

The tiger beetles (Cicindelidae) are closely related to the ground beetles (Carabidae) which appear on the next two plates.   The two families resemble each other in a number of important characteristics such as the structure and venation of the wings.

Tiger beetles, like the ground beetles, are fierce, voracious, carnivores and well equipped for a life of stalking and catching their prey.   Their long thin legs with elongate slender tarsi enable them to run very fast.   They are strong fliers and will take to the wing almost as quickly as flies when they are disturbed.   They prefer warm sandy places and on sweltering hot days they are so active that they can evade all but the most agile collector. In addition to being able to run very fast, tiger beetles are well adapted to a predatory mode of life in other ways.   For example, they have very keen eyesight and powerful mandibles.   The eyes are fairly large and lie on either side of the head.   The mandibles are enormous and have sharp points and a row of pointed teeth on the upper surface. Some Cicindelid species have enamel-like patches of white or yellow at the base of the mandibles whereas in other species this is completely missing.   The white spots, often shaded with green on the elytra, are characteristic of the genus.   Tiger beetle larvae, like the adults, are carnivorous and catch their prey in a curious and characteristic way.   The larvae excavate a vertical burrow and lie in wait for their victim with the head and thorax occupying the entrance.   When another insect ventures too close it is seized, dragged inside the burrow and devoured.   The fact that the larvae are firmly anchored by the legs and a pair of hooks on the upper side of the fifth abdominal segment enables them to overpower much larger and more powerful insects than themselves.

The family also includes several genera, such as the Madagascan *Pogonostoma*, which do not live on the ground but entirely on trees.   The members of the genus have an extremely slender body and, as a rule, a lovely blue colouration.

Cicindela chinensis DeG. *ab. japonica* Thunb., the species illustrated, is found in China and Japan.   It shows all the characteristic features associated with the mode of life of the genus *Cicindela*.

Cicindela chinensis DeG. *ab. japonica* Thunb. is exceptionally beautiful.   In most species the elytra are uniformly green with white spots, but in this case the elytra are blue and green and in addition there is a metallic reflection, all combining to produce a truly beautiful effect.

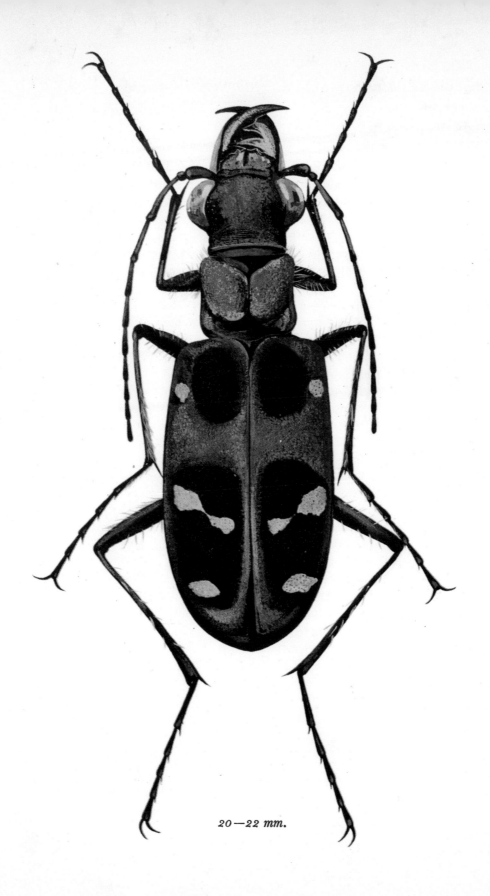

20—22 mm.

Carabus intricatus L.

Family *Carabidae*

The ground beetle family *(Carabidae)* is very large. More than 20,000 species have been described from all parts of the world. In view of their great importance in maintaining the balance of nature, their great variety of form and their great popularity with collectors the ground beetles deserve far more space than is available in a book of this kind.

Ground beetles are among the most useful insects and must have saved both governments and individuals untold sums of money by destroying pests of various kinds. Only very few ground beetles are pests. The phytophagous *Zabrus* species often cause damage to growing cereals.

Ground beetles can be divided into several groups. The tribe *Carabini* includes the larger ground beetles belonging to the genera *Calosoma, Carabus, Procerus, Coptolabrus* and many others.

The members of the tribe *Carabini* are interesting in that many are unable to fly. The wings may be only rudimentary or entirely atrophied. This fact has led to the isolation of populations and the establishment of species, subspecies and local races. More than 1,000 species and geographical races of the genus *Carabus* are known.

The Chinese species of the genus *Coptolabrus* are among the most beautiful species in the tribe *Carabini*. The elytra of these species bear raised areas which shine like exquisite green, blue, pale cream or fiery red jewels.

There are also large numbers of small ground beetles. Many of these, for example the *Nebria* species, live high up on mountain-sides and may even be found under snow. Many other species are boreophiles, relics of the glacial period, and their presence or absence in certain regions often provides valuable evidence concerning the origin of certain species.

Blind ground beetles belonging to the genus *Trechus* are found in caves in the Alps, the eastern Carpathians and the Pyrenees.

It is an interesting fact that ground beetles are primarily inhabitants of the temperate zones of the earth. Only very few species are found in tropical climates; these include *Mormolyce phyllodes* (L.) a flat, leaf-like beetle from Java, whose secretions are said to paralyse the fingers for as long as 24 hours.

The majority of ground beetles have a very attractive shape and distinct sculpture on the elytra which often serves as a means of identifying the species.

Carabus intricatus L. is a common central European species which is also found in the British Isles. It is violet-blue in colour with rugose leathery elytra. It is an example of the unobtrusive elegance typical of this family.

42

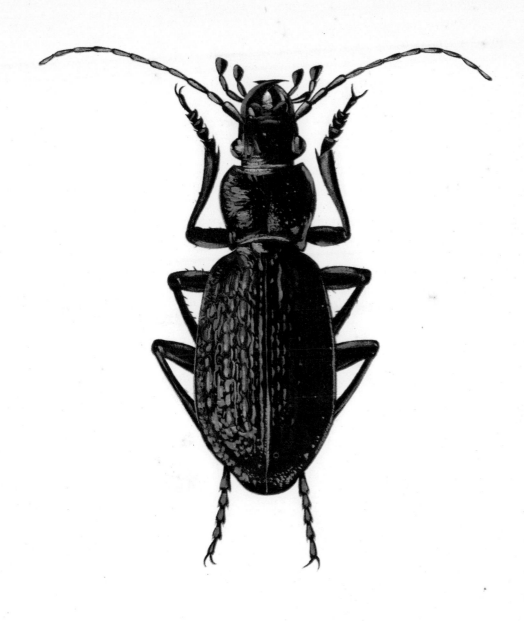

24—28 mm.

Brachinus crepitans (L.)

Family *Carabidae*

The bombadier beetle, a member of the subfamily *Harpalinae* which is widely distributed in the British Isles and Central Europe, is one of the most interesting of all insects. The interest lies not in the colour or shape; like most ground beetles the colouration is dull. The head, thorax and legs are rusty-red and the antennae, which are the same colour, are clothed with a short, rusty pubescence. The elytra are a dark blue-green with a matt lustre, and have shallow longitudinal striae with almost imperceptible punctures irregularly scattered between them.

The legs, like those of all other ground beetles, are built for speed; they are comparatively long with slender, five-segmented tarsi.

Thus there is nothing remarkable in the outward appearance of *Brachinus crepitans* (L.). However, this species is one of those mentioned in the introduction which produce a volatile secretion. It is this characteristic which has brought fame to the bombardier beetle; were it not for this ability it would be regarded as just another of the many insignificant species in the huge family *Carabidae*. This ability to 'shoot', 'explode' or 'bombard' is found elsewhere among the beetles only in the tropical family *Paussidae*, whose members live in ant and termite nests.

The bombardier beetle lives under stones at the edges of fields in warm, dry limestone areas. This species does not occur everywhere but where it does it is often present in large numbers.

Up to the present time it has always been said that the beetle, disturbed by the removal of the stone under which it lives, ejects a drop of volatile fluid from the anus, this action being accompanied by an audible explosion and a jet of smoke. Some workers believed that the explosive element was butyric acid, commonly present in the caustic secretions of ground beetles — others, that this phenomenon was caused by nitrogen derivatives. The secretions of the Paussids mentioned above contain free iodine.

New data of great interest and value were published by H. Schildknecht and K. Holoubek (1961) in the journal *Angewandte Chemie*. The authors show that the glands of the beetle secrete hydrochinon, toluhydrochinon and hydrogen peroxide. They discovered that the explosion does not occur in the air but in a special stiffened sac. The beetle discharges the secretion into this sac from the pygidial vesicle and when this fluid is mixed with the secretions from the special glands the explosion occurs. Another interesting feature is the high concentration of the different substances. Hydrogen peroxide was found to be present in a concentration of 28 per cent. Never before has such a high concentration of this substance been found in any living organism.

The ability to 'explode' is not exclusive to *Brachinus crepitans* (L.), but is found in other species of this genus whose specific names *B. explodens*, *B. sclopeta* bear witness to this habit.

This phenomenon is most decidedly defensive in character. Statements have been published claiming that the secretion has the caustic effect of nitric acid. In view of the small quantity of fluid produced by the beetle this claim is difficult to prove.

44

7 —9.5 mm.

Platambus maculatus (L.)

Family *Dytiscidae*

All the other beetles in this book are terrestrial. Several families, however, include species which live in water. The water beetles are a good example of this kind.

The water beetle family *(Dytiscidae)* is comparatively large and has a world-wide distribution. Water beetles are found mainly in still fresh water though a few species live in brackish water. These beetles are commonly found in lakes, ponds, pools and swimming pools; even the crystal clear water of springs have their own beetle fauna. In rivers they inhabit backwaters and places where there is little or no current. However, there are exceptions. Members of the genus *Hydroporus* live exclusively in the highly oxygenated waters of mountain streams where they seek out the quietest backwaters or creep into patches of water weed or moss.

Different species of water beetles differ greatly in size. Members of the genus *Dytiscus* may be more than 30 mm. long, whereas the minute beetles of the genus *Laccophilus* are only 3—5 mm. long. Some species show a marked sexual dimorphism, particularly as regards the shape of the anterior tarsus and the surface of the elytra.

Water beetles are excellently adapted to their environment; the body is boat-shaped and the legs well adapted for swimming, especially the posterior ones which serve as oars. These hind legs are flattened and the tarsal segments bear a thick fringe of stiff hairs which serve to increase the surface area. The thorax is wide and flat and the head semicircular in shape with a smooth surface. The long filiform antennae are a characteristic feature of these beetles. The extraordinary adaptation of their respiratory system to their mode of life is also noteworthy. Water beetles, like those which live on land, breathe atmospheric air. If the beetle is to remain submerged for a long time it must have a reserve supply of air. This is provided by air bubbles which the beetle carries under the elytra close to the openings of the tracheal tubes. From time to time the beetle rises to the surface of the water and thrusts the tip of its abdomen into the air, and by raising the elytra traps a fresh supply of air.

Water beetles are fierce predators and prey upon all weaker animals. They feed not only on aquatic insects but on the spawn of fish and amphibians as well. Large species of water beetles will even attack large fish.

As their large, sharp dagger-like mandibles suggest the larvae are carnivorous, and like the adults are fierce, active predators. The larvae are also well adapted to life in water in that they have legs well suited to swimming.

The species *Platambus maculatus* (L.) depicted here is found in still water in the British Isles and Central Europe. The elongate shape is characteristic of nearly all members of the family. As has already been stated in the Introduction, the colouration of water beetles is limited to a fairly small range. This species has fairly complicated markings in the colours characteristic of the family.

9 mm.

Necrophorus vespillo L.

Family *Silphidae*

The burying beetles of the genus *Necrophorus* are prominent members of the family *Silpidae*. Though they have many characteristics in common with other genera of this family there are many important differences which include not only the shape of the body but also the extremely complex mode of life.

A characteristic of the burying beetles is that they rival the scarab in the parental care that they lavish upon their offspring. Another fact is that these are the only beetles, other than the oil beetles, which undergo the complex type of development known as hyper-metamorphosis.

Burying beetles have a very distinctive appearance which makes them easy to recognise. The antennae terminate in a compact four-segmented club, and the black elytra with their transverse orange bands are short, leaving several abdominal segments exposed. They feed on small carrion such as dead mice, voles and birds. They are aided in their search for food by a keen sense of smell which enables them to locate the carrion even if it is at some distance. If the beetle is a male it first inspects the find and then climbs up to an elevated position on a stone or plant. There, using its mandibles to steady itself, it raises its abdomen in the air and emits a special odour which apparently attracts the female of the species. Of course the odour of the carrion attracts other burying beetles, both males and females; males often fight each other for possession of the carrion. The male also attracts the female by means of gritty rasping sounds which it makes with its stridulatory organ. The male then returns to the spoil and begins to excavate the earth beneath it using its mandibles to cut away obstacles such as grass roots. The dead animal slowly sinks into the earth until it finally completely disappears beneath the surface. The burying beetle digs a slanting burrow from the surface to where the carrion lies, and having reached it, begins to shape the carrion into a ball-like mass. It uses its mandibles to pluck out the fur or feathers with which it makes a kind of carpet to line the burrow. All this is done before the female arrives to lay her eggs. The female then digs a horizontal gallery leading away from the cell containing the carrion and there lays about 14 or 15 eggs. After mating and oviposition the female frequently turns on her mate and drives him away, which explains why these beetles are often found singly. After laying the eggs the female returns to the carrion and eats some of it, making a deep hole or crater in the top.

The larvae emerge after five days. They make their way to the carrion cell and climb up on the ball. Although they touch the carrion with their mandibles they do not eat it. Instead, they open their mandibles and are fed a drop of brown liquid by the adult beetle. The young larvae are very greedy and fight among themselves, even climbing up the parent's legs in the attempt to reach the mouthparts and so obtain a drop of liquid. Not until four or five days have elapsed (during which time they moult twice) are the larvae able to feed themselves. The larvae pass through three different stages before they pupate.

22 mm.

Staphylinus fulvipes SCOP.

Family *Staphylinidae*

The members of the family *Staphylinidae* usually have an elongate body and short elytra which have most of the abdominal segments exposed.   The abdomen itself is very flexible and can be curled upwards.

Rove beetles *(Staphylinidae)* are a huge family whose members can be found in all parts of the world.   At the present time more than 20,000 species are known.   Many are minute beetles living on carrion, in humus, refuse, dung, in the nests of birds, mammals and insects, in fungi, underneath stones and similar places of concealment.   This is one of the most difficult families to study.   If, in addition, we take into account the fact that the fauna of many tropical countries is almost unknown, we must assume that the number of Staphylinid species is far greater.   Certain species are able to exist in very cold climates, and are found in high latitudes: some have been found in arctic lichens.

Many species live in the nests of ants (myrmecophiles) or termites (termitophiles). There are many different types of relationship between the rove beetles and their hosts. Some species are welcome guests, others are tolerated, whilst others again behave so badly (eating the eggs and larvae of their hosts) that they are attacked and driven out by the inmates of the nest.

The large and extremely rare yellow Staphylinid *Velleius dilatatus* Mannh. lives in hornets' nests in hollow trees.

Some Staphylinids live in very damp places such as the muddy banks of rivers and ponds.   These include various species belonging to the genus *Stenus* and the colourful *Paederus* species which exude poisonous secretions that can cause inflamation of the mucous membrane of human beings.   Members of the genus *Oxyporus* are frequently found in fungi and minute *Oxyporus* and *Atheta* species are found in moss and pine needle debris in forests.   Species belonging to the last mentioned genus are exceedingly difficult to identify.

It is impossible to enumerate all the different genera of this vast family and the varied habitats in which they are found.   It is true to say that the *Staphylinidae* have a very wide and varied range of food both of plant and animal origin: many are occasional predators.

Staphylinus fulvipes Scop., the Central European species illustrated, is very rare and lives at high altitudes.   It clearly illustrates the characteristic appearance of the members of this family.   As its name suggests, this species has yellow legs.   The head, thorax and elytra are a shiny metallic blue-green and the abdomen dull black.   Though many Staphylinids are much more colourful, this species shows the relativly dark colouration which is predominant in this family.

13 mm.

Dictyoptera aurora (HERBST)

Family *Lycidae*

Dictyoptera aurora (Hbst.) has a very wide distribution. It is found throughout Europe and North America where it is also found, albeit in small numbers, in the far north. Comparison of European and North American species has not revealed any differences. This is the only Lycid with such a wide distribution.

Dictyoptera aurora (Hbst.) is a typical example of the ancient family *Lycidae* whose members are suspected of being poisonous. They are mimicked by beetles of other families as well as insects belonging to other orders. In South America the Lycids are mimicked by the *Cleridae Platynoptera goryi* Cast. and *Platynoptera lycoides* Spin. In Africa members of the genus *Tenerus* and beetles of other families, leaf beetles, weevils and longicorns do the same, as do the Brazilian Buprestids *Agrilus dilaticornis* Kerr. and *Agrilus stenocerus* Gory.

The flattened antennae are characteristic of the family *Lycidae*. The thorax, which is also often flat, is crossed by ridges forming cells or areolae. The rhomboid areola in the centre of the thorax is characteristic of the higher systematic category to which the genus belongs. The unusual appearance and structure of the elytra is of interest. The soft, extremely fragile elytra are always fairly flat and have longitudinal ridges or carinae with delicate transverse ridges joining them. Together these longitudinal and transverse ridges form a distinct network. In other Lycidae the elytral sculpture is wrinkled or irregular and in a few cases it is much reduced. In some species the sculpture of the elytra is concealed by a thick decumbent pubescence. At the present time little is known about the *Lycidae*. Members of the family are found in all parts of the world, but chiefly in the tropics where they inhabit virgin forests. They occur in Australia but not in New Zealand.

An interesting feature of the Lycids is their colouration. Most species are bright red, orange or yellow, frequently combined with black, colours which predaceous insects avoid. The Lycids are particularly in need of this warning colouration for their movements are extremely slow and irregular.

In the *subfamily Homalisinae* only the males, like some fireflies, have wings. The females, which are extremely rare, are wingless and bear a marked resemblance to the larvae.

Dictyoptera aurora (Hbst.) which has been known under the names 'Dictyopterus' aurora and *Eros aurora*, especially in the older American literature, belongs to the more sober species of Lycids as regards shape and the colour of the elytra. Both sexes have wings and well developed elytra which are widened at the tip. The thorax and elytra are the same colour, a deep, rich red. This species, like all other lycids, lives in forests. It inhabits damp places at the edges of clearings where it may be found crawling slowly and sluggishly over the leaves.

It is fairly abundant in Central Europe, but occurs less frequently in Northern Europe, England and the United States of America.

52

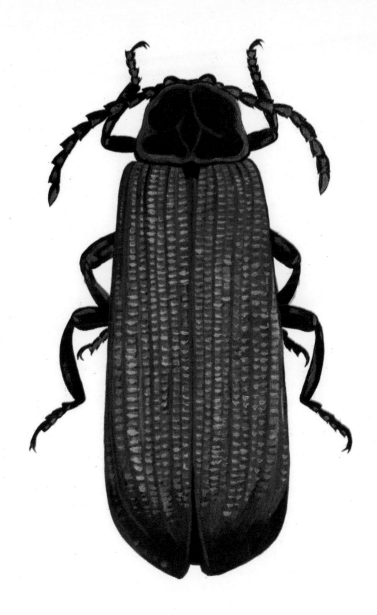

11 mm.

Lycus trabeculatus GUÉRIN.

Family *Lycidae*

The peculiarities of form found in the **Lycidae** may be seen at their most extreme in this African species. *Lycus trabeculatus* GUÉR., may be regarded as one of the most highly specialised members of the family.

The margins of the prothorax are turned sharply upwards and there is a rhomboid groove on the raised disk. The convex discs of the prothorax are separated from the lateral upturned areas by a distinct groove. Ridges, however, are not present, and the surface of the prothorax is not divided into areolas: the rhomboid groove might, perhaps, be regarded as an areola.

The elytra are the most interesting feature of this beetle. They are usually broad, circular and leaf-like, with slightly drawn out, rounded tips, and serve to protect the wings. (See also the picture showing the underside of the beetle.)

The elytra have only two longitudinal ridges; the first lies close to the slightly depressed suture and the second above the outer edge of the abdomen. Only in the space between these two ridges in each elytron does the sculpture show any sign of regularity; elsewhere it is completely haphazard and displays a slight similarity to the veination of the leaves of dicotyledenous plants. The sculpture of the underside of the epipleurae is irregular. The epipleurae lie parallel to the upper surface. The lateral margins of the elytra where they join the epipleurae are swollen. The swellings are hollow and filled with air, a device which provides strength without weight. The tips of the elytra are not swollen; they correspond exactly to the shape and rise of the wings and the purpose they serve — that of wing covers — is obvious.

The basic colour of the elytra is yellow-brown. They bear a brown pattern and the tips are coloured two different shades of brown. Although the elytra do not lack the typical yellow colour of the Lycids the general impression is one of a soft harmonious brown without any suggestion of black.

The beetle's shape also bears witness to the fact that this is a case of protective and not of warning colouration. *Lycus trabeculatus* GUÉR., is an extreme example of widening of the elytra. There are, however, numerous beetles, particularly in the African fauna, which show a tendency towards this characteristic widening, though in a more moderate form. Little information is available concerning this phenomenon. The entire family of Lycids constantly confronts us with many new and strange riddles.

25 mm.

Calopteron brasiliense CASTELNAU.

Family *Lycidae*

The specimen which served as a model for the illustration was found in Minas Gerais, Brazil, in 1897. Although the Lycids' bodies are very fragile, these beetles, if properly looked after, can be preserved in perfect condition for the same length of time as those with more strongly sclerotised bodies. A collection of *Lycidae* is very beautiful and fascinating. Besides the wide variety of shapes it is noteworthy for the red, orange and yellow colouration, frequently combined with black, which is characteristic of the family.

The species *Calopteron brasiliense* Cast. and numerous other allied species are distinguished by an unusual dull brown colouration. Even so, the typical Lycid colouration is still in evidence for the margins of the thorax and the shoulders of the elytra are orange. The elytra bear a transverse band where the delicate venation alone is coloured orange while the spaces between the veins are colourless and translucent.

The dark brown antennae are greatly flattened. The thorax lacks areolae but is divided into two sections by a sharp longitudinal ridge. Each elytra bears four prominent longitudinal ridges. The spaces between the ridges are divided by low ridges into a double row of more or less quadrate areolae.

The genus *Calopteron* includes a large number of species which are very similar in appearance. Members of this genus are frequently mimicked by other beetles living in tropical forests. It would seem that it is not only the 'poisonous' colours, which are not strongly developed, but also the characteristic shape of the body with the curiously flattened elytra, that serve to ward off enemies.

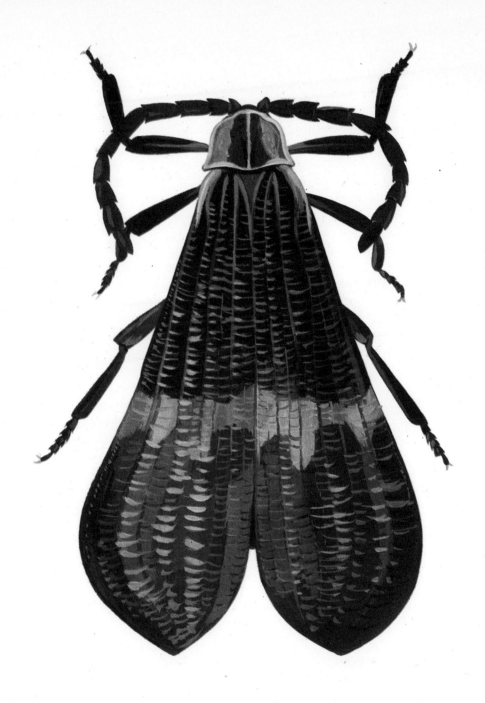

15 mm.

Phausis splendidula (L.)

Family *Lampyridae*

The cold, mysterious light produced by members of the firefly family *(Lampyridae)* is well known. In fact most people are better aquainted with the light, which, on warm June evenings rises slowly from the ground only to settle down again a short distance away, than with the beetle itself. Poets, with whom a swarm of fireflies is very popular, would be very surprised at the grey and sombre appearance of the insects. Fireflies are dull yellow-green, brown or olive coloured beetles with soft leathery bodies. In a few species, the thorax is more brightly coloured. Little is known of fireflies in comparison with other beetles. However, one thing is certain, and that is that there is something strange about the family. Only the males of this *Phausis splendidula* (L.) have wings and are able to fly.

The females, which resemble the larvae, crawl about slowly and laboriously.

The larvae of the *Lampyridae* live in damp places where they prey upon snails. The great entomologist, J. H. Fabre, was the first to observe and describe a glow-worm larva attacking a snail. The larva has long, thin, hollow mandibles which it uses to inject a digestive enzyme into the snail. This enzyme causes the body of the snail to liquefy, thus enabling the larva to suck it out of its shell. It is unknown whether this behaviour is common to all *Lampyridae*. The adult beetles have a very short life span, and it is believed that they do not feed at all.

The light of the adult male is known to attract the female, but this is not an entirely satisfactory explanation of the phenomenon as the larvae, which are sexually immature, are also luminous. Since they are the most conspicious feature of the *Lampyridae*, these organs have naturally been studied in great detail. In the male depicted here the luminous organs can be seen as two transverse dirty creamy-yellow marks of the abdomen.

These organs which lie under the translucent cuticle layer are well supplied with tracheae and nerve fibres. The inner layer which serves as a reflector contains numerous crystaloids in the form of urate crystals clustered in a large number of cells.

The actual chemical process which produces the light consists of the oxydation of a compound organic substance called luciferin by an enzyme-like substance known as luciferase. The reaction takes place within the light-producing organ. Oxygen is supplied by the tracheae and the 'command' to 'light the lantern' is given by an impulse conveyed by the nerve fibres. The intensity of the light is increased by the reflector layer. The light emitted by these insects does not contain any ultraviolet or infra-red rays.

Phausis splendidula (L.) is widely distributed in Central Europe. It is frequently to be found in large numbers at the edges of forests. It is an interesting fact that it does not occur in the British Isles although the larger Central European species *Lampyris noctiluca* (L.) and the rare and fascinating species *Phosphaenus hemipterus* (Goeze), in which the male is wingless and has only very short elytra, are to be found there.

58

8—10 mm.

Malachius bipunctatus (L.)

Family *Malachiidae*

Many species of the family *Malachiidae*, which closely resemble one another, frequent flowers, and despite their small size enhance the beauty of the flowering plants.

Tha elytra of *Malachius bipunctatus* (L.) are rich dark green with red tips. The puncturation of the elytra is so minute, shallow and sparse that it is almost invisible to the naked eye, to which the elytra always appear to be brightly metallic.

Some species show a marked sexual dichroism, the elytra of the males differing in colour from those of the female. The family also includes several species with bright red elytra.

The thorax is bicoloured and quite flat. It conceals curious and extremely interesting organs which are found in no other beetles and which probably serve to ward off enemies. These organs are in the form of retractable bladders. When the beetle is at rest the bladders lie hidden from sight on the underside of the prothorax close to the anterior margin. However, when the beetle is disturbed it thrusts out two pairs of bright red, irregularly shaped bladders which contrast strongly with the bright metallic green of the elytra. In addition these organs, which are basically tubular glands, seem to exude a secretion with a strong odour so that there is a two-fold deterrent effect. A nervous impulse probably causes a rise in the pressure of the haemolymph, which inflates the bladders to several times their original size and forces them out from under the prothorax. The evil-smelling liquid is probably discharged mechanically at the same time. When the cause of irritation disappears the bladders are retracted so that they are once more completely invisible.

The first segments of the antennae bear red lobe-like appendages whose function is at present unknown.

Many genera belonging to the family *Malachiidae* lack thoracic bladders. The family includes a large number of small and minute beetles with soft fragile elytra that crumple very easily.

Despite their small size the *Malachiidae* are very handsome beetles whose colouration is often bright and variegated. They live in flowers and their larvae are predaceous and therefore useful, but on the whole little is known of their habits and life histories.

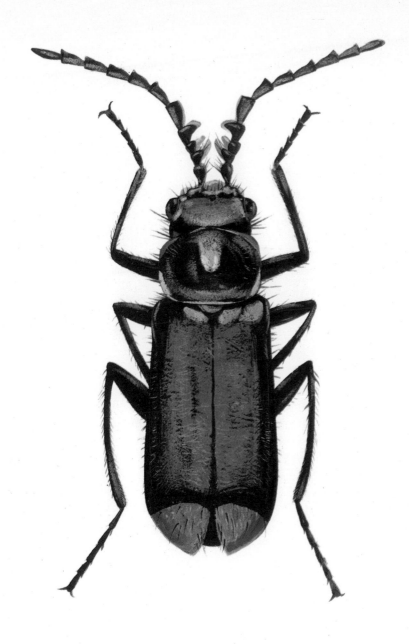

6 mm.

Anthocomus bipunctatus HARRER

Family *Malachiidae*

That beautiful colouration and great size do not always go together is proved by the appearance of many members of the family *Malachidae*.

In addition to the genus *Malachius* with its curious defensive mechanism (see page 60 for details) the family includes a large number of small and minute beetles. A characteristic feature of this family is the beautiful, bright colouration which, because of the small size of the individuals, is not immediately apparent and can be appreciated properly only with the aid of a lens.

These beetles are not only beautifully coloured but many have interesting and unusually shaped bodies. Some Mediterranean species have interesting protuberances on the head, and other species, including *Anthocomus bipunctatus* Harrer depicted here, have the elytra notched in a characteristic manner.

Anthocomus bipunctatus Harrer is one of the smaller, though not the smallest Malachiid. It has delicate pectinate antennae without any trace of the membranous projections found in species belonging to the genus *Malachius*. The head is wide with fairly prominent eyes. The thorax is flat, wider than long and more or less transversely elliptical in shape; it is the same colour as the head and both the thorax and the smooth leathery elytra lack any visible microsculpture. The elytra are red with a distinct black pattern in the form of humeral patches and a transverse band.

The most interesting feature of the elytra is the way they are notched at the tip. Near the suture and at the outer edge of the notch there are short, spine-like projections: in the centre, growing from underneath, there is a pale orange membranous projection.

The legs of *Anthocomus bipunctatus* Harrer are also of interest. They are comparatively long and thin: the femur and tibia of the first pair are pale coloured whereas in the second pair only the femur is pale, the tibia and tarsus being black. The last pair of legs is entirely black.

Anthocomus bipunctatus Harrer is a fairly common species yet little is known of its life history and habits. The significance of the notches on the elytra is unknown. The handsome beetles belonging to the family *Malachiidae* merit a far greater share of attention than they have received up to the present time.

3 mm.

Melyris granulata REDT.

Family *Melyridae*

The genus *Melyris* is a member of the distinct, but not particularly large family *Melyridae*, which occurs only in the tropics and warmer regions of the temperate zone. In the western part of the palaearctic region members of this family are found only around the Mediterranean. *Zyras oblonga* F. is another member of the family. It was introduced into Hamburg by ships from the Mediterranean.

According to some systematists the family *Melyridae* includes not only the Melyrids themselves but also members of the *Malachiidae* and *Dasytidae* but this is a matter of personal opinion. There is no doubt that there is a very close relationship between the *Dasytidae* and *Melyridae* and that the latter has numerous features in common with the *Malachiidae*. Even so, the general appearance of the beetles suggests that each of these groups is an independent family. This is especially evident when one compares members of the *Melyridae* and *Malachiidae*.

The *Melyridae* may be recognised very easily by their general appearance. They have characteristic longitudinal ridges on the elytra which are usually either blue or green, though in a few species the elytra have a yellowish tinge.

Melyris granulata Redt. is a Mediterranean species widely distributed in North Africa and especially common in Algeria.

This species has comparatively short, slightly serrate antennae and a fairly large, somewhat elongate head. The eyes are very small and lie some distance from the base of the antennae. The thorax is flat and wide with well defined lateral margins; it has an interesting sculpture consisting of low ridges giving the appearance of fine graining. The hard convex elytra are comparatively short and broad. Each elytra bears three well defined longitudinal ridges which unite at the apex. The ridges are less shiny, and so appear darker than the spaces between them. These interspaces bear a double row of well defined punctures, but as these punctures are irregularly spaced there are no transverse ridges.

Melyris granulata Redt. is entirely dark blue with a dull metallic sheen. Only the areas between the elytral ridges are slightly shinier.

This example is of particular interest as the sculpture of the elytra has a slight resemblance to that of some species of *Lycidae*.

6 mm.

Thanasimus formicarius formicarius (L.)

Family *Cleridae*

The family *Cleridae* is a comparatively large one containing more than 3,500 species. Members of this family are found in all parts of the world, the greatest number of genera and species occuring in the tropics. The geographical range of each species is limited. Some isolated island territories such as Madagascar and New Zealand have their own endemic fauna. However, certain species belonging to *Necrobia, Thaneroclerus, Tarsostenus* and other genera have been introduced with imported goods and become established in new areas.

The Clerids are very lively, active beetles with eleven segmented antennae which are usually serrate or end in a slender club. The tarsi are five-segmented though they often appear to be only four-segmented. Although the family includes several species which are not brightly coloured, most of the Clerids are distinguished by their bright attractive colouration. The elytra show a wide range of pastel colours whose beauty is enhanced by the thick pubescence, often arranged in transverse bands, present in the majority of species.

Some species mimic certain Lycids. Reference to this phenomenon is made in the introduction. Only very few species are found in large numbers; on the whole these beetles are extremely rare.

The Clerids are predaceous beetles which feed on other insects. They are found on trees, either on or under the bark, or, less frequently, on flowers. Some species, especially certain members of the genus *Necrobia*, may be found on carrion and other materials on which they do not feed; they are there because they prey upon the insects which feed on these substances. It has been shown that these beetles devour *Dermestes* larvae and that they sometimes attack hams and other preserved meat. It is interesting to note that they have been found in Egyptian mummies.

Thanasimus formicarius formicarius (L.) is the best known and most common species. It is a very useful species for both the elongate pink larvae as well as the adult beetles feed on certain extremely destructive bark beetles, and are in fact their most important natural enemies. When bark beetles increase in number there is a corresponding increase in the numbers of *Thanasimus*.

Thanasimus formicarius formicarius (L.) is widespread throughout the whole palaearctic region. It is able to stand very low temperatures and is found as far north as Scandinavia. Other species are found in Sakhalin, Kamchatka and northern Canada.

In spite of the fact that very similar and closely related species are found in the U.S.A., this species failed to establish itself when it was introduced in an attempt to control bark beetles by natural means.

66

7—11 mm.

Trichodes horni WOLC. ET CHAPIN

Family *Cleridae*

Members of the handsome, brightly coloured genus *Trichodes* are extremely fascinating beetles for several reasons, the main one being that the larvae of one of these insects, so it is believed, gave rise to the scientific name by which the whole family is known.

Aristole was the first to use the name '*Kleros*' for the small grub which lives in beehives. His description may refer to the larva of *Trichodes* or to the wax moth, or it may be composite with the addition of a few mite characteristics. Later workers used this name for the larvae of the beetles we now call *Cleraidae*, and in time the Greek term '*Kleros*' was latinised and used as the root for the family name.

The genus *Trichodes* is interesting for other reasons. The adults of many species belonging to this large genus do not live on trees but are found on flowers, especially those of umbelliferous plants. Like all Clerids they are predaceous and attack various insects which are found in flowers (floricolous insects). Some species even attack the harmful locust. The life history promises to be of great interest, though few details are known at the present time. It has been shown that the larvae undergo their development in beehives. It appears that the eggs in some way become attached to the bees who carry them to the nest. The larvae which hatch out undergo a normal complete metamorphosis. In this they differ from the oil beetles whose triangular larvae attach themselves to the bees and undergo hypermetamorphosis in the nest. Although some members of the genus *Trichodes* are found in large numbers in warm southern climates, very little is known of their life history for the study of the genus presents many difficulties.

Another interesting characteristic of this genus is its unusual distribution. There are over 90 described species of which the majority are found in the palaearctic region, chiefly in the warm areas of Southern Europe, North Africa, Central Asia and Asia Minor. A few species occur in colder regions, *T. apiarius* (L.) is found in Northern Europe, *T. ircutensis* (Laxm.) in Siberia and *T. sinae* (Champ.) in Northern China, Korea and Japan. About 70 species are palaearctic, 12 occur in North America, while only 10 are found in tropical Africa. *Trichodes* beetles are unknown in other parts of the world.

The American species are particularly interesting and remarkable. Some show certain resemblances to various palaearctic species while others show a distinctive and independent line of evolution.

The rare species *Trichodes horni* Wolc. & Chapin depicted here is found in Arizona and southern California. Its colouration is most unusual in that the elytra are tri-coloured whereas most species belonging to this genus have two-coloured elytra.

12—15 mm.

Dieropsis quadriplagiata GAHAN

Family *Cleridae*

That *Dieropsis quadriplagiata* Gahan is a very rare species is shown by the fact that only very few specimens are to be found in collections. This beetle, which is quite large with a distinctive body shape and bright black and orange in colour, has a number of unusual characteristics which set it apart from other Clerids and indeed from all other beetles.

Dieropsis quadriplagiata Gahan is the only described species known to have the eyes divided into two adjacent areas of differently sized ommatidia (the lenses which form the compound eye of an insect). The two areas are divided by a transverse line. Divided eyes are also found in the whirligig beetles *(Gyrinidae)* which are able by this means to see both above and below the surface of the water, and in a number of longicorns, but in each case all the ommatidia are the same size. The structure of the eye of *Dieropsis* closely resembles that of members of the fly *(Diptera)* genus *Bibio*. These flies have eyes of a similar type but the arrangment of the different sized ommatidia is the reverse of that found in the African Clerid *Dieropsis*.

Another unusual character of *Dieropsis quadriplagiata* Gahan is the structure of the front legs. The tibiae are clothed with thick pubescence; the tarsal segments are not lobed.

At the present time little is known of the habits of *Dieropsis quadriplagiata* Gahan. The structure of the eyes and legs seem to suggest that the beetle lives mainly on trees and bushes where it moves about actively in search of its prey. On the ground it is probably far less active. It has huge, well developed wings and is probably a strong flier.

This beetle is entirely black except for the orange bands on the elytra and yellow patches at the side of the prothorax. The antennae are short, terminating in a large flattened club similar to that found in the genus *Trichodes*.

Dieropsis quadriplagiata Gahan shows a number of characteristics, such as the huge front legs, the interesting tarsi and the curious divided eyes, which are found nowhere else in the Cleridae. This species has certain characteristics in common with members of the subfamily Clerinae, yet it differs in so many ways that a separate subfamily should be created for it.

27 mm.

Hylecoetus dermestoides (L.) ♂ *var. marci* L.

Family *Lymexylidae*

The beetle illustrated shows a curious feature which is characteristic of the family *Lymexylidae*, also known as the *Lymexylonidae*.

The maxillary palpi of this family show strongly developed sexual dimorphism. The females have palpi of the type normally found in beetles, whereas in the males (see illustration) the last segment is greatly enlarged. It is divided into a row of branches which are so thickly covered with sensory bristles that they resemble brushes.

It is generally believed that these palpi serve as olfactory organs and help the males to find the females. There is no doubt that the large number of sensory bristles greatly increase the efficiency of this organ. The palpi may be regarded as a sort of 'olfactory radar' which is effective even over great distances.

The sexual dimorphism displayed by this species does not end here. In both the male and female of the typical form the thorax and elytra are reddish-brown with the tips of the elytra darker in colour. Two colour varieties are always smaller than the typical form. The elytra of the colour variety *marci* L. depicted here are brownish-yellow with dark brown tips. The elytra of var. *morio* Fabr., on the other hand, are entirely black.

Hylecoetus dermestoides (L.) is often regarded as a timber pest because the larvae drill holes in the wood, but in reality the damage caused by this species, which is not especially common, is slight.

The family *Lymexylidae* is not large. Its members are elongate and cylindrical in shape. It is probably very old from an evolutionary standpoint, and some authorities regard it as a separate superfamily.

Little is known of the life history. Some workers believe that the beetles may undergo a hypermetamorphosis similar to that found in the family *Micromalthidae;* though up to the present time this has not been definitely proved.

13 mm.

Semiotus distinctus HERBST

Family *Elateridae*

The click beetles *(Elaterioae)* are well known for their elegant torpedo-shaped bodies. The posterior angles of the prothorax are often drawn out into sharp points. The members of this family are not only elegantly shaped, but many are also brightly coloured and attractively patterned. There are of course many species which are entirely brown or black.

The *Elateridae* are well known for another characteristic which is common to almost all species. When laid upon their backs these beetles are capable of leaping into the air and landing upon their feet. The means by which this is done is as follows. A spine on the posterior margin of the underside of the prothorax catches against the edge of a groove on the anterior margin of the mesothorax. When the beetle lies on its back it moves the prothorax in such a way as to cause the spine to slip into the cavity and this in turn causes the elytra to press against the surface and project the beetle into the air. This action is often accompanied by a clicking sound — hence the name click beetle.

Click beetles are phytophagous and are usually found on flowers or other parts of plants. When faced with real or apparent danger they draw in their legs and fall to the ground where they can hide in the maze of vegetation. Should they fall on their backs, a position which renders many insects helpless, they give a swift leap and are soon on their feet again. This ability to leap into the air has doubtless saved the life of many a click beetle.

Most Elaterid larvae, often called wire-worms, live in the ground and often cause a great deal of damage to cereal crops by feeding on the roots. They are elongate and cylindrical with a hard creamy-yellow or yellow-brown cuticle. The last segment is often darker and more strongly sclerotised than the rest of the body. Its shape varies with the species and provides a useful means of identifying them.

This Brazilian species *Semiotus distinctus* Herbst is a good example of the brightly coloured members of the family. The proportions of the elongate thorax and elytra are very satisfying and the clearly defined pattern on the elytra, which bear longitudinal rows of punctures, all combine to produce a harmonious whole.

The *Elateridae* are a very large family with representatives in all parts of the world, though they are most numerous in tropical and subtropical regions. The vast number of species and their great resemblence to each other makes the study of these beetles extremely difficult.

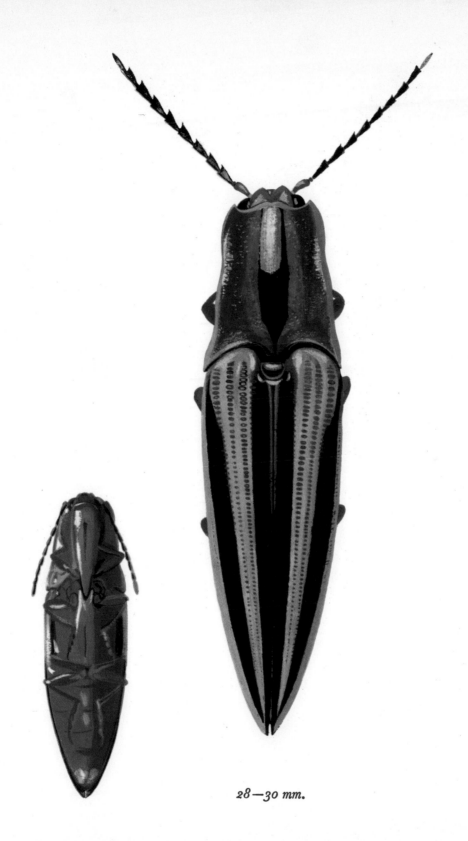

28—30 mm.

Chrysochroa edwardsi HOPE

Family *Buprestidae*

The *Buprestidae* are a large family of beetles which resemble the click beetles *(Elateridae)* in shape. However, they lack the thoracic spine and groove device which enables the Elaterids to leap into the air.

The family includes many exceedingly handsome, often metallic species. The *Buprestidae* have very hard, thick cuticle. The majority of species live in the tropics, usually in the treetops or on the creepers, which climb from the twilight of the forest into the bright light of the sun. They are extremely active and like the hottest sunshine. The brilliant elytra, whose magnificent colours are the result of interference and refraction of the sun's rays, have been described as a kind of mirror which reflects the light and thus protects the beetle from the heat. Even the species which live in temperate regions are most active in hot summer weather.

All *Buprestidae* are phytophagous. The white legless larvae, which have a broad prothorax, live in and feed on plant stems and branches of trees and bushes; some species make galleries in leaves. These beetles are sometimes regarded as pests, but in fact they are of minor importance for they attack only diseased, dying or dead trees, bushes and other plants.

It is interesting to note that the scientific name of the family dates back to Aristotle. The Greek word *Buprestos* means 'killer of cows'; Aristotle probably used the name for certain members of the family *Meloidae* whose bodies contain poisonous substances which can injure grazing cattle. (See page 102). At a later date the name was used for other beetles, namely the harmless, non-poisonous *Buprestidae*. The family name of the soldier and sailor beetles *(Cantharidae)* arose in a similar way. Aristotle used the term *Kantharos* for the Meloid oil beetles which are entirely different from the soldier and sailor beetles.

The Buprestid pictured here, *Chrysochroa edwardsi* Hope, which is common in India and Assam, is a beautiful example of the family. The upper surface is metallic green with a bronze or coppery reflection here and there. The cream-coloured patches which lie just behind the middle of the elytra are bordered with a metalic violet-blue colour. The predominating colour of the underside is a metallic red-gold. This species is comparatively large and so its beauty is immediately apparent. *Chrysochroa edwardsi* Hope glows like a jewel and is an adornment to any entomological collection.

76

50 mm.

Anthrenus scrophulariae (L.)

Family *Dermestidae*

Many members of the family *Dermestidae* though attractive to look at, are dangerous and destructive pests. These small or moderately sized beetles are 2—9 mm in length. They are flat or convex elongate-oval in shape. The elytra are clothed with a thick pubescence or scáles. The antennae terminate in a distinctive flat club. In addition to the compound eyes some species have a median simple eye or ocellus.

Out of doors some species are found under the bark of trees, in bird nests, on carcasses and especially on the remains of the skin of birds and *mammals*. Other species, such as *Anthrenus* are found on flowers. Many *Dermestidae* have become serious pests and may often be found in large numbers in food warehouses. They also cause damage to woollens, hides and furs. Certain species are amongst the most dangerous enemies of zoological and entomological collections.

Anthrenus is one of the worst offenders in this way. At first the specimens attacked do not show any unusual symptoms. By the time a fine brown powder is seen underneath the insect it is usually too late to save the specimen, of which nothing remains but the outer shell. A neglected collection in which Dermestids have flourished is a sad sight. Pins bare, or with only a wing or other small part of the body sticking to them, are all that remain.

It is probably true to say that men have made collections of natural history specimens for the last three hundred years, yet few insect collections have survived, mainly because effective insecticides were unknown and *Anthrenus* and other pests allowed to multiply unchecked. To this day both individuals and museums are waging a never-ending battle with this pest.

Anthrenus museorum (L.) is the most common species, but the larger and more colourful *Anthrenus scrophulariae* can cause just as much havoc in a collection. *Anthrenus verbasci* (L.), *A. fuscus* (Ol.), *A. pimpinellae* (F.), *A. olgae* Kalík and others are almost as bad.

Bird nests in the roofs of houses are frequently the source of an infestation within the house, where Dermestids often cause serious damage to furnishings and clothes.

4 mm.

Tenebrioides mauritanicus L.

Family *Trogositidae*

As is apparent from its name, Mauretania is the original home of this beetle. Today, however, it is cosmopolitan and found in food warehouses in all parts of the world. It is a representative of the small yet very interesting family *Trogositidae*. The names *Ostomidae*, *Ostomatidae* and *Temnochilidae* have also been used for this family. The family includes many species of widely differing anatomical structure whose relationship has been discovered only by very detailed study of the anatomy.

Outdoor members of this family are found chiefly in old wood and under the bark of trees. *Tenebrioides mauritanicus* L. is only occasionally found out-of-doors. It is most common in warehouses where both the adults and larvae cause a great deal of damage.

Tenebrioides mauritanicus L., when it lives out-of-doors is predaceous, feeding on insects which live under bark. Although it is sometimes predaceous in warehouses, it also attacks cereals and flour, dried fruit, tobacco and chicory roots. Both adults and larvae cause damage by boring through wrappings and the fine sieves used in flour mills.

The female lays piles of white eggs in foodstuffs and in cracks in the fabric of the warehouse. The number of eggs varies between 30 and 50. The larvae which hatch out easily gnaw their way through ordinary wrappings and are even able to make their way through tin foil. The larva, which moults three or four times, is white with dark brown eyes and mouthparts. There is a dark x-shaped spot on the first thoracic segment. The following two segments have four dark round patches and the last abdominal segment bears two brown horn-like spines or cerci.

The larval stage lasts about 110 days at a temperature of 18°C. When it is fully grown the larva seeks a suitable spot in which to pupate and there it spins its cocoon. On the average the prepupal stage lasts about ten days and the pupal stage one month. The pupa is creamy-yellow in colour and about the same size as the adult. The adult remains in the cocoon for a few days before emerging to begin its search for food.

The duration of the life cycle, from egg to adult, is 177 days at a temperature of 18°C. The adult may live for as long as 668 days.

The useful predatory habits of this species are far outweighed by the damage it causes to stored food. Infestations are controlled by means of insecticidal sprays, contact poisons, and in the case of very large scale infestations by fumigation with methyl bromide and hydrocyanic acid.

6—11 mm.

Glischrochilus quadripunctatus (L.)

Family Nitidulidae

The Nitidulids are a very large, widely distributed family which includes some extremely small beetles. Most species are convex and either oblong or elongate-oval. The elytra are usually abbreviated, leaving the tip of the abdomen exposed. The antennae are eleven-segmented in the majority of species and always terminate in a compact, three-segmented club.

Some Nitidulids are serious pests. This is particularly true of the huge genus *Meligethes* which includes many species which appear completely identical and which are almost impossible for a non-specialist to identify. *Meligethes* species are found mainly on cruciferous plants and occur in vast numbers wherever these plants are cultivated.

Nitidulids are found also on stored food. *Carpophilus* species have been recorded from a wide range of foodstuffs including raisins, figs and drugs.

Many species live out-of-doors and are important from an economic viewpoint. These include many members of the genus *Epurea* which feed on fungi but occasionally attack other insects and especially soft, defenceless larvae. Despite their small size they are handsome beetles and many species have attractively marked elytra.

Glischrochilus quadripunctatus (L.), is often referred to in the literature under the name *G. quadripustalatus* (L.). In older classifications the Nitidulids were frequently classed as Bark beetles. They often occur on trees where they feed on sap.

Glischrochilus quadripunctatus (L.) differs from other Nitidulids in a number of ways, but chiefly in that the elytra are long and cover the whole abdomen.

Librodor quadriguttatus (F.) closely resembles *Glischrochilus quadripunctatus* (L.) but may be distinguished from it by the fact that it lacks the furrows on the forehead between the antennae which are present on the latter.

The species illustrated occurs throughout central Europe and locally in England. It is a comparatively rare species.

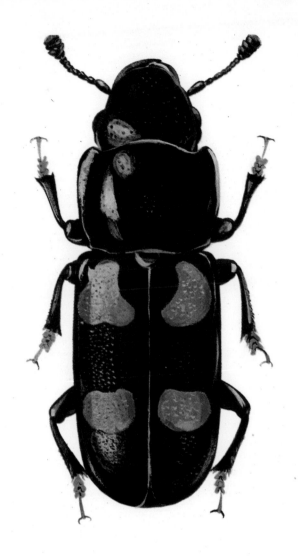

3—6.5 mm.

Cucujus coccinatus LEWIS

Family *Cucujidae*

Cucujus coccinatus Lewis is one of the many beautiful and interesting beetles which occur in Japan.

The Cucujids show a number of interesting characteristics and adaptions to their mode of life. *Cucujus coccinatus* Lewis is a corticolous species (one that lives under bark). The elytra, and also the head and thorax, are dorso-ventrally flattened and enable the beetle to creep into narrow cracks and crevices which they would not be able to reach if they were more convex. The *Cucujidae* have eleven-jointed, filiform antennae which may terminate in a slender, indistinct club.

The Japanese *Cucujus coccinatus* Lewis is a free-living species. The black head and prothorax are thickly punctured with coarse deep pits. The head, which widens out behind the eyes, is triangular with blunt posterior angles. The prothorax bears two shallow longitudinal grooves separated by a ridge and encircled by a raised line. The lateral margins of the prothorax are dentate, a characteristic common to all members of the family. The bright vermilion elytra are parallel-sided with a well marked suture. The spaces between the inconspicuous longitudinal ridges have an irregular sculpture which is no coarser than the puncturation of the head and prothorax. The surface of the elytra lacks pubescence, except at the tips, which are sparsely clothed.

Like all other free-living Cucujids the Japanese *Cucujus coccinatus* Lewis has a very local distribution. Its diet appears to be a mixed one, consisting of decaying plant and animal matter. The large mandibles, however, seem to suggest that it may be an occasional predator attacking smaller insects which live under bark.

The family *Cucujidae* includes a member of genera whose members are found more frequently in warehouses than out-of-doors. Many of these have become cosmopolitan, having been transported with food to all parts of the world. It is interesting to note that these cosmopolitan species are smaller and less colourful than those found out-of-doors.

II—I3 mm.

Erotylus incomparabilis PERTY

Family *Erotylidae*

Members of the family *Erolytidae* are found all over the world but they are most common in the tropical regions. Only relatively few species are found in the temperate zones and besides being small they are not particularly colourful. That is why the Brazilian species *Erotylus incomparabilis* PERTY from the Amazon valley has been chosen to represent this family.

An important diagnostic character of the family is that the eleven-segmented antennae are inserted at the sides of the forehead at some distance from the edges. The thorax may be convex or flat but always has a distinct margin. The legs are comparatively long and thin: the first and second pairs of legs have globular coxae. The tarsi are usually four, but sometimes five-segmented, with the first three segments slightly widened and pubescent beneath. The last segment bears a simple claw. The elytra completely cover the abdomen which consists of five segments of approximately equal size.

The *Erotylidae* feed on fungi, usually those found growing on trees. Many tropical species bear bright distinctive markings of red, yellow and black. This is known as a 'warning' type of colouration. It is not known whether the *Erotylidae* are in fact poisonous and have a true warning colouration, or whether they are non-poisonous beetles with a protective colouration. It is known, however, that they are avoided by insectivores who are frightened off not only by the colours but also by the evil-smelling fluids secreted by these insects.

This Brazilian species is a very good example of the beautiful tropical Erotylids. The shape of the flattened thorax, with its slightly undulating surface, resembles that of some members of the family *Silphidae*.

The structure of the antennae is also of interest. They consist of a number of thin, elongate, shiny-black segments; the last three segments are dull black and flattened to form an elongate club. The antennae are reminiscent of those found in the *Lycidae*. The basal third of the elytra, near the shoulders, is broad and raised and the remainder falls away steeply to the tip: this can be seen most clearly when the insect is viewed from the side. The elytral sculpture consists of regular longitudinal rows of punctures.

The illustration shows the beautiful bright elytral markings of red, yellow and black found in the tropical species of this family.

20 mm.

Ailocharia mirabilis MOTSCH.

Family *Coccinellidae*

Ladybird beetles *(Coccinellidae)* are widely known and great favourites. Almost everyone is familiar with these brightly coloured creatures which have made a place for themselves in rhymes, poems, songs and stories.

The family has a world-wide distribution. Many species are tropical, but a large number of attractive species are found in the temperate zones.

All ladybirds have round or broadly elliptical bodies with strongly convex elytra. The head is very small and almost completely hidden under the prothorax. The antennae are usually eleven-segmented and terminate in a three-segmented club.

Ladybirds have characteristic lanceolate larvae which are usually dark with spots of yellow or some other bright colour, and many bear pubescent warts and spine-like or branched outgrowths. The larvae have three pairs of comparatively long legs and are fairly active. The pupae of some species hang head downwards, attached by the tip of the abdomen to the cast of larval skin, while those of others remain attached to this skin along their entire length.

The life history and habits of *Coccinella septempunctata* (L.), the seven-spot ladybird, has been studied in great detail. Members of this species have the curious habit of congregating in large numbers in winter hiding places (hibernation) and also during hot weather (aestivation). The reason for this has not yet been explained satisfactorily. Some entomologists believe that assemblages of this kind help to increase the effect of the warning colouration. When disturbed, ladybird beetles exude a yellow, pungent and apparently caustic secretion, and for this reason they are left severely alone by insectivores.

Ladybirds are true friends of man, and especially gardeners, for they destroy large numbers of greenfly and occasionally also attack other insects. A seven-spot ladybird in the High Tatra mountains was observed eating the mountain may-fly *Ameletus inopinatus* Eaton. It is a great pity that this useful insect is often killed by people who mistake it for certain leaf beetle pests. Some species of ladybird beetles have been employed successfully in the biological control of insect pests and have been introduced and become established in infested areas.

12 mm.

Endomychus coccineus (L.)

Family *Endomychidae*

The *Endomychidae* live mainly in the tropics; only a few species are found in the temperate zone.

They are closely related to the ladybird beetles *(Coccinellidae)* though this is not immediately apparent in all species. Whereas certain *Endomychus* species resemble the ladybirds both in shape and colour, members of the other genera are quite different. The rare species *Lycoperdina bovistae* (F.), for example, looks like a small version of *Blaps (Tenebrionidae)* while *Sphaerosoma* and *Mycetaea* species resemble certain *Erotylidae*.

The *Endomychidae*, whose members differ so much from one another, all have the following characteristics: — The antennae are comparatively long, usually eleven-segmented and frequently terminating in a three-segmented club. The coxal cavities of the first pair of legs are always open behind. The coxae of the first and second pair of legs are globular. The tarsi are four-segmented, though they may appear to have only three segments. The abdomen is five- or six-segmented.

The curious and extremely rare *Phleganophorus bispinosus* Hampe which lives in ants' nests also belongs to this family. This species has most extraordinary broad antennae resembling those of certain *Paussidae*.

Endomychus coccineus (L.), the European species illustrated here, has antennae which terminate in a slender, indistinct club. The head is black and the thorax red with a central black spot. The elytra are also red with four large black spots. The colouration and the indistinct elytral puncturation give it the appearance of a ladybird, but on closer examination the distinctive Erotylid characteristics are at once apparent, and with a little practice it becomes easy to distinguish members of the two families.

Endomychus coccineus (L.) occurs under the bark of dead deciduous trees, and especially in beeches and elms with fungal growths. This is an unusual mode of life for members of the *Erotylidae*: with the exception of a few which live in trees almost all other species live in fungi and especially puff-balls.

Although many species belonging to this family are very small, they display a number of very interesting characteristics.

6—7 mm.

Bostrichus capucinus (L.)

Family *Bostrichidae*

The Bostrichidae are cylindrical beetles which live in the wood of felled trees and dry timber. They are occasionally found in growing trees, but attacks are usually limited to weak or diseased trees.

Certain species cause a great deal of damage to timber in tropical regions and especially in Africa. The *Cteridae*, in particular members of the genus *Cylidrus*, are the natural enemies of these timber pests.

A number of different names have been used for this family which makes it very difficult to trace it in the literature. The name *Bostrichidae* applies to the beetles described here, while *Bostrychidae*, whose spelling differs only by a simple letter, is a synonym of the name *Scolytidae* (bark beetles). A great deal of the older literature on 'Bostrychids' in fact deals with bark beetles, and to make matters worse, some recent workers have used the old term *Bostrychidae* when referring to this family.

Bostrichus capucinus (L.) is a typical member of the family. The elongate cylindrical shape, which is frequently found amongst beetles living in wood, is characteristic of the *Bostrichidae*. The head is almost completely hidden by the overhanging, swollen thorax. The thorax has a rough rugose surface and bears a number of sharp tooth-like projections on either side near the anterior angles. Both the head and prothorax are black, and the latter, though it has a rough surface and is clothed with a short black pubescence, appears quite shiny. The antennae are comparatively short and terminate in a distinct, slender, loose, three-segmented club. The scutellum is small and black. The cylindrical elytra are red-brown in colour; there is a faint indication of a ridge near the suture but elsewhere the surface bears irregularly scattered punctures of uneven size. Femora and tibiae are black while the tarsi are slightly brownish in colour.

Bostrichus capucinus (L.) is a central European species found in great numbers in the forests of the Carpathian mountains. It is very rare in England. It is a good example of how a species which is prized as a great rarity in one place may be extremely common in another.

9—11 mm.

Hedobia imperialis (L.)

Family *Anobiidae*

The *Anobiidae* are better known by repute than in real life. The reason for this is the curious, tapping sounds produced by the so-called death-watch beetles which are believed to fortell the early death of the hearer. It is interesting to note that this superstition is found in almost every country. The fact that the ticking sound, which is not very loud, was heard only in the quiet of the night by old and sick people probably strengthened this belief. The tapping is in fact a mating call made by the male striking his head on the sides of the gallery in the wood in order to attract the attention of the female.

The *Anobiidae* include a number of pests of stored food such as the bread or drug-store beetle, *Stegobium paniceum* (L.), which is able to multiply very rapidly and is capable of doing a great deal of damage to stored cereals and other substances. It also attacks specimens in herbaria and entomological collections.

The larvae of the death-watch beetle (*Xestobium rugovillosum* DeG.) often cause extensive damage to the woodwork of old buildings, but it appears that they do not attack the timber unless there is a fairly high moisture content. The larvae of *Anobium punctatum* DeG. (furniture beetle) are the well known woodworms. Other beetles, such as *Xyletinus* which occurs in old dry tree stumps, *Ernobius* species which live in pine cones, and *Ptilinus* which is often found in old cottages, are less harmful. Members of the genera *Dorcatoma*, *Caenocara* and *Anitys* have short round bodies. They live in puff-balls and other fungi.

Many species show a distinct sexual dimorphism.

Most of the beetles belonging to this family are fairly small, few measuring more than 5 mm. *Hedobia imperialis* (L.), the species illustrated here, is one of the largest species in the family. It is an attractive beetle with chocolate brown elytra which are clothed with a thin white tomentose pubescence. The thorax is also pubescent. Like all members of the family *Hedobia imperialis* (L.) has fairly long filiform antennae and comparatively long legs. It occurs out-of-doors and can usually be found by beating old hedges. Once again we see that even small beetles can be very attractive to look at.

94

3·5—5·5 mm.

Niptus hololeucus (FALD.)

Family *Ptinidae*

Despite its small size the golden spider beetle (*Niptus hololeucus* Fald.) is one of the largest species in the interesting family *Ptinidae* whose members are all between 1 — 5 mm. long. Some species are dull and uninteresting in colour whereas others are attractively patterned. In many species it is difficult to distinguish the male from the female but a few species show a marked sexual dimorphism. Most Ptinids have a small head and prothorax and a large globular abdomen which is entirely covered above by the elytra. They have long thin antennae and relatively long stout legs. Out-of-doors the Ptinids occur on decaying plant and animal matter, but they are also found in houses and warehouses. Some species, including *Niptus hololeucus* (Fald.), are household pests with a cosmopolitan distribution.

This species has strongly convex elytra which appear circular in shape when viewed from above. The beetle itself is a dull yellow-brown, but is clothed with a pubescence which gives it its characteristic golden sheen.

Niptus hololeucus (Fald.) is mainly a pest of stored food such as tea, tobacco, cereals, bran, cocoa, medicinal herbs and drugs. They have also been recorded in woolen blankets, feathers, old bones, paper and even in old books.

After mating the female lays 15 — 20 eggs which, under normal conditions, hatch out after about 16 days. The white cylindrical larvae feed for about 80 days before they pupate. Although an infestation may be limited to a small area, a much larger quantity of food than they actually attack is rendered unpalatable. Pupation takes place within a cell. The pupal stage lasts 20 days and the adult beetle remains within the cell for a further 20 days before emerging. The whole cycle from egg to adult takes about 136 days, but may be much longer if the pupae hibernate.

This pest can be exterminated by various means which depend upon the type of goods infested. In food stores D.D.T. powder may be used, or fumigation with methyl bromide or hydrocyanic acid. Fabrics may be protected by paradichlorbenzene fumes. As these insects are able to withstand only a limited range of temperature it is possible to kill them by heat treatments. A temperature of 50°C for half an hour is sufficient to kill this pest.

4.5 mm.

Pyrochroa coccinea (L.)

Family *Pyrochroidae*

Only 100 species belonging to the cardinal beetle family *(Pyrochroidae)* have been described. They are all bright scarlet or red in colour, and as they are avoided by insectivores it would seem that this serves as a warning colouration.

The adult beetles have a prominent head which is narrowed behind the eyes. The long serrate or pectinate antennae are eleven-segmented. The base of the thorax is narrower than the elytra, which, with their bright colour and rounded tips, are the most conspicuous feature of the Pyrochroids. The abdomen is six-segmented in the males and five-segmented in the females.

The beautiful scarlet elytra of *Pyrochroa coccinea* (L.) are clothed with a thick short red pubescence which gives them an unusual dull gloss. They lack any other ornament or sculpture. The thorax is also scarlet, while the underside, legs, scutellum and head are black. The head has a small red raised area between the eyes.

Pyrochroa coccinea (L.) is a Central European species. It occurs in deciduous forests under the bark of large tree stumps and on common forest plants.

The large, flat Pyrochroid larvae are yellow-brown in colour. They have huge mouthparts; the last abdominal segments are strongly sclerotised and the last one bears a pair of sharp projections. The larvae are found under the bark of large deciduous tree stumps, usually low down near the roots where it is damp. There is something very curious about these larvae. According to the literature they feed on wood, and the length of the larval stage, which may be anything up to 3 years, is due to the low nutritive value of this food. However, these larvae are very active, and if touched by a pair of forceps, immediately lunge at the instrument with the mandibles. A reaction of this kind is typical of predaceous larvae. As other wood-eating larvae are extremely slow in their reactions it would seem that further investigation is required. It is quite possible that *Pyrochroa coccinea* (L.) larvae have a mixed diet. This shows how little is known of the habits and life histories of some of the more common species.

13—17 mm

Meloe variegatus DONOV.

Family *Meloidae*

This oil beetle which occurs in central and southern Europe differs from the other black or dark metallic blue species by its bright colouration.

Members of the genus *Meloe* have many interesting features. The antennae are comparatively short and moniliform, the head broad and transverse, the wings undeveloped and the elytra dehiscent (gaping apart towards the tips) so that abdominal segments are exposed. The abdomen, in comparison with the rest of the body is unusually large. This is especially true of the gravid females in spring when their movements are much restricted by the swollen, heavy, egg-filled abdomen.

The female digs holes between 2 and 3 cm. deep in the ground and lays several batches of yellow eggs. She may lay more than 10,000 eggs. This vast number is necessary to ensure the survival of the species for very few larvae survive to develop into adult beetles. The oil beetles undergo the form of development known as hypermetamorphosis. The tiny, active larva with two long cerci which hatches out of the egg is known as a triungulin because each leg bears three claws. Linnaeus and Réaumur believed that the triungulin was a kind of louse. Linnaeus named it 'Pediculus apis' or bee louse. It was later placed in a genus called *Triungulinus*. It was not until some time later that Newport discovered that it was the first larval stage of the oil beetle. The triungulin climbs up the stems of plants and lurks in the flowers waiting for a bee to alight. When the bee arrives, the triungulin attaches itself to the legs or underside and is carried to the nest. Large numbers of larvae attach themselves to the wrong kind of insect and thus meet an untimely death. Once it reaches the nest the larva relinquishes its hold on the bee and makes its way into a cell filled with honey or pollen. When the cell has been closed it devours the egg. It then moults, shedding the long cerci, and reappears with a hard head capsule and stout legs. When the larva has consumed the contents of one cell it moves to another. Here it undergoes further changes until finally it has no legs and is known as a pseudo-chrysalis or pseudo-pupa. Later, either in the same or in the following year, it enters the true pupal stage.

This phenomenon of hypermetamorphosis is characteristic of the *Meloidae* and certain members of related families. The first stage larva which emerges from the egg varies in appearance with different species. The first stage larva of *Apulus muralis* (Forst.) does not have three claws, and lacks cerci. For this reason some authorities consider the name triungulin inappropriate and recommend the use of the term 'primary larva'.

Oil beetles contain a large quantity of oily, yellowish haemolymph which they exude when disturbed. Acute nausea may be caused by food contaminated with this fluid.

Meloe variegatus Donov. is one of the rarer species of the genus. It is very rare to find more than one specimen at a time.

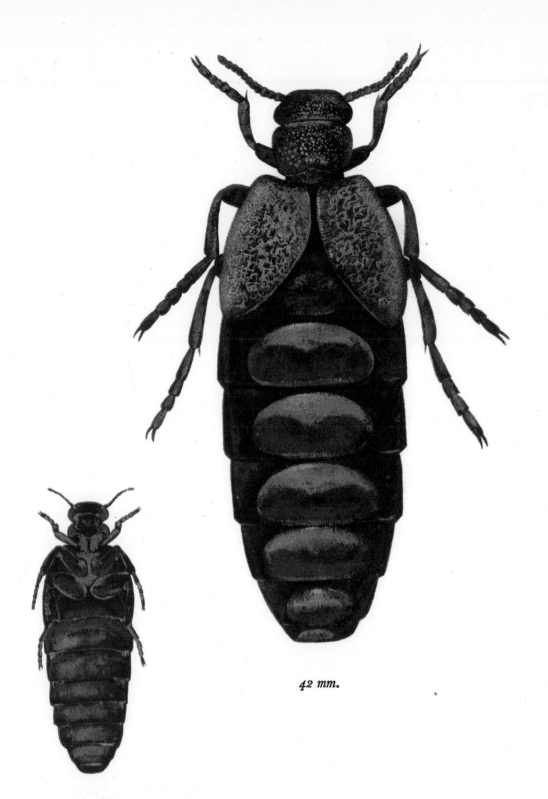

42 mm.

Lytta vesicatoria (L.)

Family *Meloidae*

Lytta vesicatoria (L.) is the well known, and it might almost be said, notorious Spanish fly. This was one of the few insects known and used by the medical practitioners of the Middle Ages and perhaps even in ancient times. Like all other Meloids this species contains the poison known as Cantharidin ($C_{10}H_{12}O_4$) which has been used for centuries for many and varied purposes.

The Spanish fly contains more cantharidin than any other member of the family. Though it is difficult to tell from the old medical prescriptions exactly which species were used, it is certain that these included a number of species belonging to *Mylabris* and other related genera. Some old medical books contain descriptions of the beetle, stating that it has yellow stripes on its wings. This is not true of the Spanish fly but certain *Mylabris* species answer to this description.

Cantharidin is found mainly in the elytra but it has also been shown to exist in the genitalia and the haemolymph, though in a less concentrated form.

Cantharidin, when administered in small doses is supposed to act as a powerful aphrodisiac, and it was an important constituent of many 'love potions'. Modern research has shown that this substance is very harmful to the kidneys, but it is occasionally prescribed for external application in the form of compresses and poultices. Large doses of cantharidin can cause death and this property was made use of by the Medicis in the 'aqua tofana' which they served to their enemies under the cloak of hospitality.

Lytta vesicatoria (L.) is an attractive, metallic green beetle. The elytra may have a blue or red reflection. It occurs throughout southern and central Europe and is also found in the British Isles. It has been recorded in central Ireland. Adult beetles are found on willow, ash and other trees. Where they occur in large numbers these beetles have an unpleasant mouse-like smell. The larvae, like those of other *Meloidae*, undergo hypermetamorphosis in the nests of social hymenopterous insects. *Lytta vesicatoria* (L.) lays between 2,000 and 10,000 eggs near the entrance of *Anthophora* or *Colletes* nests. The primary larvae hatch out after 23 to 30 days and make their way into the nest where they continue their development.

As can be seen from this short account, *Lytta vesicatoria* (L.) is an extremely interesting species, especially as regards its habits and life history.

20 — 22 mm.

Cerocoma muhlfeldi GYLL.

Family *Meloidae*

Although the space available in a book of this size is very limited, the *Meloidae,* because of their many peculiar and interesting characteristics, receive preferential treatment at the expense of other families.

It would be impossible to leave out the fantastic *Cerocoma muhlfeldi* Gyll. which occurs mainly in southern Europe. The soft emerald green elytra with their granular surface and long, thick, decumbent yellow pubescence have the delicate sheen of a valuable brocade.

The middle and hind legs with their long, thin tarsal segments are in no way unusual. It is the front pair which merit attention. The tibiae are flattened and look as though they were broken or deformed: the tip is enlarged, and there is a curious pointed process just above the tibio-tarsal articulation. The tarsi are flattened and the individual segments have characteristic shapes which are not found elsewhere amongst the beetles.

The head is of the normal Meloid type, round and sharply constricted behind the eyes. The antennae are one of the most unusual features of this beetle. They are so greatly modified that it is impossible to count the number of segments. Their whole structure is so twisted and there are so many projections and indentations that they defy description. They can be seen in the illustration. The thorax is elongate with a deep depression on each side near the anterior angle.

Cerocoma muhlfeldi Gyll., a European species related to *Lytta vesicatoria* (L.) has antennae whose curious shape not only equals but even outshines the bizarre antennae of the tropical *Paussioae.*

17 mm.

Metoecus paradoxus (L.)

Family *Rhipiphoridae*

The *Rhipiphoridae* are perhaps the most interesting of all beetle families. They are widely distributed throughout the world but as a rule they are extremely rare and little is known about them.

The Rhipiphorids are parasitic beetles which live on hymenopterous and orthopterous insects. The best known European species is *Metoecus paradoxus* (L.) illustrated here. This species displays both sexual dimorphism and dichroism. The male in the picture has a yellow-brown thorax with a black central mark, while the female has a black thorax with diagonal yellow marks at the side. The antennae of the male are long and flabellate; those of the female are short and pectinate. In both sexes the elytra narrow towards the apex so that they do not meet at the tips and leave the membranous wings exposed. The legs are very long and thin.

The life history of *Metoecus paradoxus* (L.) is very remarkable and resembles that of the *Meloidae* in many respects. The primary larva (triungulin) which hatches out of the egg makes its way into a wasps' nest where it undergoes its development first as an internal parasite and later as an external parasite of the wasp larva. *Metoecus paradoxus* (L.) can undergo its development only in underground nests and some authorities go so far as to claim that it can develop successfully only in the nest of *Vespa vulgaris* (L.), but not in that of *V. germanica* (F.) which also builds its nest underground. Wasp species which build their nest above are immune from attack by *Metoecus*.

Metoecus paradoxus (L.) is unusual in that it is the only member of the family *Rhipiphoridae* which preys on the larvae of social insects. Other Rhipiphorids attack solitary *Hymenoptera*. The fact that *Metoecus paradoxus* (L.) is a parasite of social wasps explains its fairly common occurrence and has enabled workers to study its life history and habits.

Other members of the family *Rhipiphoridae* such as *Rhipidius* and *Rhipiphorus* are extremely rare. Very often only the host species is known and all other details of the life history remain to be discovered.

Many species have well developed membranous wings though the elytra are reduced to mere scales. Members of the genus *Symbius* show considerable modifications suited to a parasitic mode of life. The male is a winged beetle-like insect whereas the female is worm-like and never leaves the body of the cockroach in which it lives.

Some taxonomists are of the opinion that the *Rhipiohoridae* are closely related to the *Strepsiptera* (which are sometimes known as *Stylopidae*) whereas others regard them as entirely separate families.

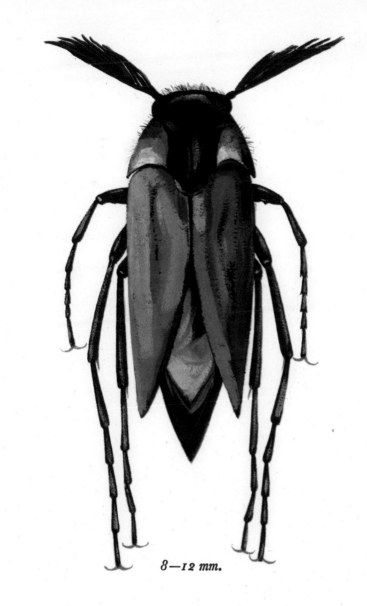

8—12 mm.

Mordella villosa (SCHRANK)

Family *Mordellidae*

The *Mordellidae* are a family of fairly small beetles, usually black in colour, which live in meadow flowers. They are extremely agile and difficult to catch, either taking to the wing or slipping out from between the fingers. Normally the beetle moves slowly over the surface of the flower, but if it is disturbed it turns on its side and moves about very swiftly. This is made possible by the structure of the body; the thoracic and abdominal segments are compressed laterally to form a median ventral keel and the tip of the abdomen (with the single exception mentioned below) is drawn out into a long process called the style. It is by making rapid jabs with the style that the beetle moves forward. The legs are comparatively long and slender.

The best known genera are *Mordella*, *Mordellistena* and *Tomoxia* which has a shorter stouter style.

The beetles belonging to these genera are either entirely black, black with silver or gold tomentose vestiture, yellow-brown with the tips of the elytra somewhat darker (*Mordellistena neuwaldeggiana* [Panzer]) or brown with a yellow pattern on the thorax and elytra as in *Mordellistena femoralis* (L.). *Mordellistena abdominalis* (F.) is unusual in that the thorax of the males differs in colour from that of the females. The thorax of the male is black, like the elytra, whilst that of the female is bright red.

Anaspis is another species found in flowers. It resembles other *Mordellidae* in general shape, but as it lacks a style its movements when trying to escape are rather different. Many species are brown or black, but some have a transverse orange band near the base of the elytra and others have a black pattern on a yellow background. Some taxonomists are of the opinion that the *Anaspis* should be transferred from the *Mordellidae* to *Scraptiidae*, a closely related family.

The handsome European *Mordella villosa* (Schrank) which is sometimes known as *M. fasciata* (F.) shows all the typical Mordellid characteristics. The elytra are patterned with an attractive golden tomentose pubescence.

The *Mordellidae* are a very difficult family from a systematic point of view. Many species are extremely difficult to separate. This is one of the reasons why the details of the life history and habits of the family are unknown.

9 mm.

Akis bacarozzo (SCHRANK)

Family *Tenebrionidae*

The genus *Akis* belongs to the family *Tenebrionidae* which includes a vast number of species differing greatly in size and shape.   Most Tenebrionids are brown or black though there are a few brightly coloured species.

The majority of Tenebrionids are slow-moving creatures, feeding on all kinds of decaying organic matter.   Most species may be regarded as useful scavengers but a few, including *Tenebrio molitor* (L.) and members of the genus *Tribolium*, are pests of flour and other stored food products.

The Tenebrionids are amongst the few animals which are able to live and thrive in some of the most arid and desolate deserts of Africa and Central Asia.   They feed on dead blades of the sparse grass and their water supply is provided by traces of moisture retained in the roots.   Many *Pimelia* species are found in the desert.

The *Tenebrionidae* probably show the widest range of size and shape to be found within a single family.   Indeed they give the impression of trying out all possible, and even a few impossible types of body form.   Many genera resemble members of other families.

Tenebrionids are most numerous in tropical and subtropical regions.   Some are halophiles, that is they show a preference for places with a high salt content.

Members of the genus *Akis* are found chiefly in the Mediterranean region and more rarely in south-eastern Europe.   Their occurrence is closely linked with the warm Mediterranean climate;   they do not occur even in very hot places in Central Europe.

Akis bacarozzo (Schrank) is a fairly common Italian species found in cellars and similar places.   The body is slightly flattened and the posterior angles of the prothorax are drawn out into sharp spines.   The anterior half of the elytra is level while the posterior part slopes downward to the tips.   The epipleurae are separated from the rest of the elytra by a sharp ridge so that seen in cross section the body is almost triangular.   There is a row of granules near the lateral margin of the elytra, and in some specimens these are separated by oblique wrinkles.

20 mm.

Tribolium destructor UYTTENB.

Family *Tenebrionidae*

This nocturnal species was described by the Dutch entomologist, Uyttenboogaart in 1933. Its country of origin is unknown. After the Second World War it was introduced into many countries with foodstuffs and by 1952 this species had been recorded from Holland, England, Hungary, Germany and Czechoslovakia, and by now it is probably even more widespread. An account of its life history has been published by Czechoslovak entomologists.

Tribolium destructor Uyttenb. is a warehouse pest: it attacks flour, nuts and other foodstuffs of a similar nature.

The small, dark, rather ordinary-looking species *T. confusum* Duval has one very curious characteristic. It produces a secretion whose chemical properties are such that they can cause the crippling of the beetles' own offspring. The adult beetles exude minute drops of an oily yellow fluid which crystallises on their bodies; when they are irritated these drops vapourise. If some of this liquid touches the body of a larva crawling nearby, or if a larva is enveloped in a cloud of vapour, then the beetles into which they develop either have fewer antennal segments or are completely devoid of antennae. If the larva in question is about to pupate, the mouthparts of the pupa turn black, and the adult emerges without these vital organs. In its crystalline form this secretion kills all young larvae, or if it comes in contact with the legs or antennae of older larvae it gives rise to monstrous two- and three-branched legs and antennae in the adult. If the victim is a pupa, the beetle emerges a freak, half adult, half pupa. If the pupae come in contact with this substance just before the beetle emerges, the adult will lack the black pigment melanin and have a flexible white cuticle. (See Roth & Howland, 1941: Ann. Ent. Soc. Am. *34* 151—172.) In 1943 Alexander and Barton discovered that the active substance causing these curious phenomena was ethylquinone.

It may be assumed that similar substances are present in other species of this genus. It is interesting to note that laboratory broods of *Tenebrio molitor* (L.) show a high percentage of deformed individuals. It is quite possible that the discovery of ethylquinone in the secretions of *Tribolium destructor* Uyttenb. will help to explain the origin of abnormalities in other species.

3—5 mm.

Scarabaeus sacer (L.)

Family *Scarabaeidae*

This species has already been discussed in some detail in the introduction.

Scarabaeus sacer (L.) is remarkable for the parental care it bestows upon its offspring. The same characteristic is found not only in other members of the genus but in certain species of related genera as well.

The scarabs, both adults and larvae, feed on the droppings of cows, horses, donkeys and other animals. The broad fossorial front legs enable them not only to handle the dung but to dig in the ground beneath it. The beetles are generally found in the ground beneath or directly under the dung rather than in the dung.

When the beetle lays up a food store for itself it digs a slanting burrow into which it drags the dung. It may prepare several stores of this kind. However, it follows a different procedure when the food is intended for its offspring. In this case it first makes a small ball the size of a walnut and this is rolled about until it becomes the size of a man's fist. This process has its anxious moments: a passing scarab may offer to help his hardworking friend and for a while they roll the ball together. However, if the owner is not careful his assistant may suddenly make off with his property. Generally, however, he notices in time and sets out in pursuit of the thief, and if the latter is caught he immediately pretends to be trying to save the ball from running away by placing himself on the side away from the owner. They then continue their labours in complete harmony and without any show of displeasure by the owner who would have behaved in exactly the same way if the position were reversed.

When the ball has reached a suitable place it is buried in the ground and the female lays her eggs in it.

The scarab's actions are entirely instinctive but it is not at all surprising that in ancient times man believed not only that the scarab was capable of rational behaviour but was also governed by supernatural forces. It follows naturally that it became an object of worship.

Scarabaeus sacer (L.), as can be seen in the illustration, is entirely black. As it was frequently idealised in ancient Egyptian carvings, it will not be amiss to familiarise oneself with its true appearance.

35 mm.

Phanaeus conspicilatus WB.

Family *Scarabaeidae*

The species illustrated is a visible proof of the fact that the lamellicorn beetles of the family *Scarabadeiae* display an apparently inexhaustable range of shape and colour. Many also have curious and interesting habits.

Not only *Dynastidae* and *Lucanidae* (stag beetles) but also many *Scarabadeidae* bear extraordinary projections on the head and thorax. These structures, which may be very large, are found chiefly in the males. The female may possess similar structures but they are usually less well developed and in some species they are entirely absent.

In the case of the Dynastids and Lucanids these projections serve mainly as weapons in their jousts for the female and are used only very occasionally for holding on to branches. The *Scarabaeidae* seem to use these horns to pull food into their burrows.

Phanaeus conspicilatus Wb. is a beautiful South American species from tropical Columbia. Like all other true scarabs it has a broad flattened head and fossorial anterior tibiae. It uses the head as an excavator and the tibiae as shovels. By lowering its head and pushing, this beetle can move a huge mound of earth or dry dung. The eyes are set far back, at the very edge of the semi-circular head shield which bears a deep cleft just in front of the eyes so that forward vision is not impaired.

The head and the spinous, backward-pointing horn are entirely black. The colouration of the thorax and the rest of the body is much more attractive. The thoracic projections, the groove between them and the lateral margins are black. The rest of the prothorax is green with a green and black iridescence which change with the direction of the light. The elytra are just as attractive as the thorax, both in shape and in colour. They are the same iridescent green while the deep longitudinal furrows are black. The underside is black and the femora iridescent green.

The beauty of *Phanaeus conspicilatus* Wb. may well be compared to that of a precious stone.

25 mm.

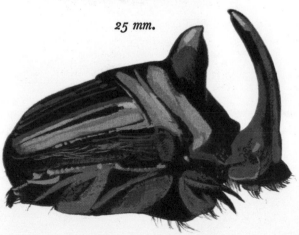

Granida albolineata MOTSCHOULSKY

Family *Scarabaeidae*

The subfamily *Melolonthiae* includes several beetles of great economic importance such as the cockchafers, *Melolontha melolontha* (L.) and *Melolontha hippocastani* (F.), which often appear in very large numbers and may cause a great deal of damage to trees of various kinds.

The cockchafers feed on the leaves and blossoms of trees. They remain in the treetops during the day and take to the wing in the evening. They make their first appearance in May, or at the end of April if the weather is unusually warm.

The females burrow 5—7 cm into the ground and there they lay their batches of 10—30 eggs. A single female will lay about 70 eggs before she dies. The larvae hatch out in about 4—6 weeks. They are cylindrical, C-shaped, with a fat abdomen and short legs. During the summer they feed on grass roots and in winter they burrow deep down into the earth. In spring they come up again and continue feeding. The larval stage lasts three years during which time the larvae moult three times. At the end of this time the adult beetle emerges, and towards evening, when the cuticle has hardened and darkened, it leaves the ground and flies to the nearest tree.

The shape of the last abdominal segments differs from one species to another: in some it is drawn out into a point and in others it is rounded.

All cockchafers are phytophagous, but many species are not injurious for they feed on plants which have no economic importance.

The Japanese *Granida albolineata* Motsch. has a very attractive colouration. Like the *Melolontha* species, it is brown, but unlike them, it has three longitudinal white stripes on the thorax and four white stripes (one short near the suture and three longer ones on the elytra.) There are also a number of small white patches. The white markings are made up of delicate short scale-like hairs. This tomentose vestiture, though found in other members of the family, is nevertheless rather unusual among the chafers.

118

25 mm.

Ranzania bertolinii (LUC.)

Family *Scarabaeidae*

The *Cetoniinae* are a subfamily of the *Scarabaeidae*. Some authorities consider that they merit family rank. Members of the subfamily are well known for their beauty and are much sought after by collectors. They occur chiefly in the tropics though a number of attractive species are found in the temperate zones. Some of the largest known beetles, members of the genus *Goliathus* belong to this subfamily.

The short, stout, white larvae live in vegetable debris; a few occur in ants' nests.

Many species are floricolous, that is they live on flowers, often of the strongly scented kind. They have heavy bodies and often move rather clumsily so that the pollination mechanisms of the flower are damaged. Fortunately they usually frequent plants of little or no economic importance. Other species feed on the sap flowing from wounded trees.

Ranzania bertolinii (Luc.) is widespread in East Africa. The head, which is well adapted for entering flowers, is white except for the flattened raised edges which are dark. The thorax is a beautiful green, not metallic as in most Cetonid beetles, but opalescent, so that every movement causes the colour to change. The broad fossorial legs, which the beetle uses to make its way into flowers, are green. The large triangular scutellum, so characteristic of the Cetonids, is the same colour. The elytra are fairly flat and lack true epipleaurae. The *Cetoniinae* are unusual in that they are able to fly with the elytra entirely or almost completely closed. The main colour of the elytra is white, a colour rare in beetles. With the aid of a lens it can be seen that the white is tinged with pale ochre and faint blue tones and also that there are minute furrows on the surface which give it a scratched or erased appearance. The white is set off by a beautiful shiny black line bordering the scutellum and running down the suture to the tip of the elytra. In addition there is a black tongue-shaped patch which runs from the shoulder to a point one third of the way down the elytra. There is an elongate elliptical patch in the apical third of each elytron. The upper surface of the last abdominal segment is also white.

This combination of colours makes *Ranzania bertolinii* (Luc.) one of the most attractive *Cetoniinae* of the African fauna.

23 mm.

Polystigma punctata MAC L.

Family *Scarabaeidae*

The Australian fauna does not lack beautiful *Cetoniinae* for the subfamily is represented by a number of distinctive species.

Polystigma punctata MacL., often called spotted dog, for obvious reasons, is widespread in Victoria. It is small in comparison to other Australian Cetonids. Like all other *Cetoniinae* it has flattened legs which enable it to force apart the petals in order to reach the sweet nectar at the base of the calyx. The colouration of the head is very interesting. Between the eyes, which lie far back on either side of the head near the anterior margin of the prothorax, there are two black stripes which run forward to a point half way down the length of the head. The head, thorax, elytra and the last abdominal segment are all the same yellow-brown colour. The thorax has a characteristic pattern: there are three black spots near the posterior margin, one in the middle and one on either side, and a V-shaped mark near the anterior angle. In some specimens this latter mark is broken up into three spots. There is a short black line on the posterior margin of the prothorax where it abuts the scutellum. The elytra are comparatively flat, without epipleurae and with the characteristic notch at the side just behind the shoulders. The elytron, like the prothorax, are patterned with black lines and spots. The black line runs around the scutellum and down the suture to the tip of the elytra. Each elytron bears a single humeral spot and three larger spots at regular intervals down the mid-line. There is a small spot outside and just below the central spot, and between the middle and last spots there is a small spot next to, and touching the sutural line.

The last abdominal segments bears a central black spot and occasionally two lateral ones. The colouration of *Polystigma punctata* MacL. though decorative, is rather dull and restrained compared with other *Cetoniinae*

18 mm.

Eupoecila australasiae DONOV.

Family *Scarabaeidae*

The Cetonid beetle *Eupoecila australasiae* Donov. which is widespread in Australia and several Indonesian islands, displays a most interesting colouration.

The head is two-coloured: the back is dark brownish-black and the front a bright yellow with two minute dark spots. The projections on the head are also darker in colour. This is a most unusual type of colouration, as a rule beetles do not show such a variety of colours on the head.

The thorax is pitchy-brown with a yellow pattern. The anterior and lateral margins have a yellow border on which there are 2—3 dark spots on each side. The posterior margin also has a yellow border, but it does not join the lateral border. There is in addition a rhomboid patch in the centre of the thorax.

The large triangular scutellum also bears a yellow patch similar in shape to that of the prothorax but larger in size.

The colouration of the elytra is variable. In some specimens two-thirds of the elytra are red-brown while the apical third is black. In other specimens the elytra are all red-brown or all black. The markings are the same colour as those of the prothorax. There is an elongate slightly S-shaped mark on the anterior two-thirds which may or may not join a transverse mark lying across the suture at the junction of the red and black ground colour. In the apical third the elytra have a yellow lateral margin which also turns a little way up the suture.

The combination of yellow with two shades of brown on the elytra contrasts sharply with the brilliant yellow and black of the underside. Yellow and black alternate on the meso- and metasternum and also on the abdominal segments which are clearly visible when the beetle is viewed from the side. When feeding on a flower the beetle frequently lies on its back or is seen from the side. Though little is known of the significance of these colours it seems possible that they may be of the warning type. The yellow and black of the underside and the markings of the elytra are very reminiscent of the colours and markings of certain hymenopterous insects.

22 mm.

Metopodontus savagei HOPE

Family *Lucanidae*

The stag beetles *(Lucanidae)* are a handsome, interesting and well known family. This is mainly because the majority of species are fairly large and many have huge mandibles. The European stag beetle *Lucanus cervus* L. is one of the best known of all beetles and one all beginners want to find.

Lucanus cervus L. is a very good example of the basic stag beetle shape. The mandibles of the male are so large and bear a number of teeth or tines, with the result that they bear a very strong resemblance to antlers. The mandibles of the female are much shorter and lack large teeth.

Metopodontus savagei Hope, an African species from the tropical forests of the Cameroons, resembles the stag beetle though it is smaller in size. The slender, slightly curved mandibles are quite long in comparison to the body. If we compare the size and structure of these two beetles, one a tropical species and the other from oakwoods in the temperate zone, it will be seen that the tropical species, contrary to popular belief, is not necessarily either larger or more extreme in shape than that from other regions.

The majority of species are tropical, though some occur in places with a more temperate climate. The most common colours in this family are various shades of brown and yellow; only very few species are metallic. Both sexes of *Metopodontus* are the same colour though the details of the pattern differ a little. In the male the dark band running down the suture narrows towards the tip whereas in the female it is the same width throughout. The size and shape of the teeth on the mandibles of the male are very variable.

Stag beetles undergo their development in old decaying trees. The life cycle generally lasts several years. Stag beetles are sometimes regarded as pests, but this is not strictly true as they do not attack strong healthy trees.

Members of this family show many individual variations, a phenomenon which is discussed in greater detail in connection with *Chiasognathus granti* Steph.

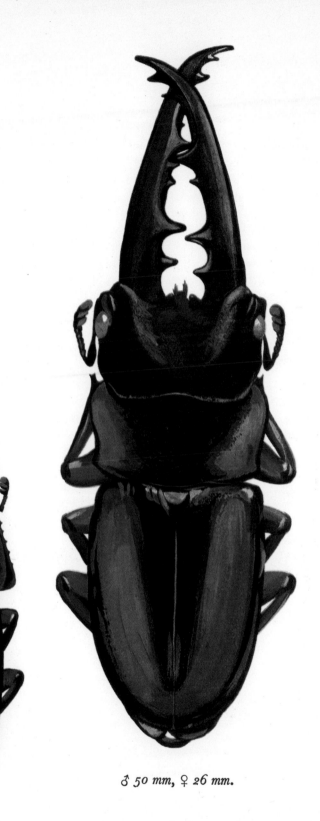

♂ 50 mm, ♀ 26 mm.

Chiasognathus granti STEPH.

Family *Lucanidae*

Not all members of the family *Lucanidae* have antlers like *Metopodontus savagei* Hope illustrated on the previous page. *Chiasognathus granti* Steph., for example, has long, toothed, sabre-like mandibles with hooked tips. The maxillae, though much shorter than the mandibles, are large with small sharp teeth along the outer edge. The antennae are unusual in that they are very long and bear a tuft of fine yellowish hairs.

The female, which is much smaller than the male, has short stout mandibles and the antennae lack the yellow tuft of hair.

In the larval stage, which may last several years, the insect feeds on decaying wood, but the adult beetles feed on sap oozing from wounded trees, using their long pubescent tongues to lick it up.

What purpose do these huge mandibles serve? The answer is that they are not used for grasping food, but play an important role in both natural and sexual selection. When large numbers of Lucanids converge on a tree to feed on the sap, they frequently fight amongst themselves and, naturally, the strongest individuals are the victors. The weaker beetles are killed or put to flight, an example of natural selection by survival of the fittest.

The males also engage in violent skirmishes to decide which is to have the female. Here again the more strongly armed specimen is the winner.

The great variation in the size of different individuals is a characteristic of the family. Of two specimens belonging to one species, one may be twice as large as the other. One of the causes contributing to this state of affairs is that if two individuals of very unequal size engage in battle the smaller often quits the fight as soon as it can. It has a chance to win only if matched against an individual of similar strength and size. This behaviour leads to the formation of 'size groups' which are apparently hereditary and are believed to safeguard the species from degeneration.

Chiasognathus granti Steph., which is widespread in Chile, is unusual among the *Lucanidae* in that it has a beautiful metallic bronze sheen on the elytra while the thorax, the base of the mandibles and the abdomen have green reflections.

♂ 65 mm, ♀ 35 mm.

Dynastes hyllus CHEVR.

Family *Dynastidae*

The Dynastids are a family of lamellicorn beetles found chiefly in the tropics. They include some of the largest beetles known, the largest of all being the South American species *Dynastes hercules* (L.). The males of this species may reach a length of 180 mm.

A conspicuous characteristic of this family is the pronounced sexual dimorphism displayed by many species. The males often bear huge hornlike processes on the head and thorax while the females have only very small processes or none at all. Spectacular examples of these processes may be seen in members of the subfamily *Euchirinae*.

The purpose of these horns is unknown, but it is likely that they serve the same purpose as in the *Lucanidae*.

The larvae are fat with short legs and live in and feed on decaying wood.

Dynastes hyllus Chevr. occurs in the southern part of the United States. The male has a single upright but slightly curved horn on the head and three in the prothorax. The middle thoracic horn is very much larger than the others and curves forwards and downwards so that its tip almost touches the horn on the head. The underside of this central horn is covered with a thick, pale yellow pubescence. The lateral horns are very small and slightly curved. All three horns are black, like the parts of the body from which they arise — i.e. the head and the anterior margin of the prothorax. The rest of the prothorax is a pale greyish green with the raised lateral and posterior margins narrowly black. The triangular scutellum is fairly large and rich dark brown in colour. The stout legs are pitchy-black. The outer edge of the tibiae are denticulate and they are broad and fossorial at the apex.

The mouthparts are well adapted to the feeding habits, that is for licking up sap from wounded trees, a habit which these beetles share with the *Lucanidae*.

The elytra are smooth and shiny without any marked sculpture. The ground colour is almost the same as the prothorax, though slightly darker. The suture and the outer margin of the elytra are dark. There is a longitudinal row of minute spots near the suture and the rest of the surface is speckled dark brown.

The family characteristics are not especially well developed in *Dynastes hyllus* Chevr. which is illustrated here as an example of the North American fauna.

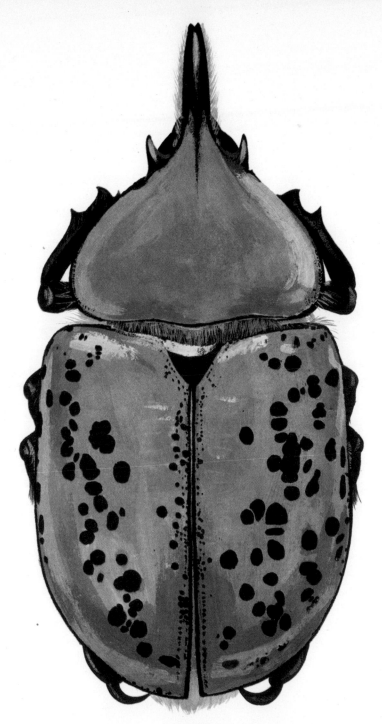

55 mm.

Sternotomis pulchra (DRURY)

Family *Cerambycidae*

The *Cerambycidae* are a large family: more than 16,000 species have been described from all parts of the world. They are very popular with collectors, which is not surprising as they show a very wide range of colours. This fact has made it very difficult to decide which species to include in this book.

Most longicorns have slender bodies, though some, like the members of the subfamily *Prioninae* are comparatively short and broad. One of the most striking characteristics of the family are the long filiform antennae which may be as long or longer than the beetle itself. Members of a few genera, such as *Polyarthron* and the South American *Polyoza* and *Microplophorus* have pectinate antennae. Some longicorns, for example the genus *Necydalis*, have abbreviated elytra which have the membranous wings exposed. Species belonging to the genera *Clytus* and *Plagionotus* have normal elytra which are patterned with yellow bands so that they resemble certain wasps.

Longicorns vary greatly in size. As a rule they are moderately large or large, but there are some small and very small species. Some of the tropical species are amongst the largest beetles known. Specimens of *Titanus giganteus* L., *Xixuthrus heyrovskyi* Tippman and *Macrodontia cervicornis* L. may be more than 100 mm. long.

All longicorns have four-segmented tarsi.

There are many cases of mimicry in this family. These species closely resemble members of other families such as the *Lycidae* whose members are left unmolested by insectivorous birds and lizards, and the *Erotylidae* which are avoided by insectivores because of their foul-smelling secretions.

Certain longicorns produce their own protective strongly-smelling secretions. The shiny green European species *Aromia moschata* (L.) produces a penetrating musky odour.

Longicorns are phytophagous. Some feed only on the soft parts of plants but others have very powerful mandibles which enable them to gnaw their way into very hard wood. A number of species are harmful and capable of causing a great deal of damage.

Sternotomis pulchra (Drury), illustrated here, is a pest of coffee in West and Central Africa and especially in the Congo. The delicate pastel hues of this beetle are not appreciated by the owners of coffee plantations as the larvae feed on the twigs with the result that the bushes dry up and yield less coffee. *Sternotomis variabilis* Qued., a related species with green and black transverse stripes, causes similar damage.

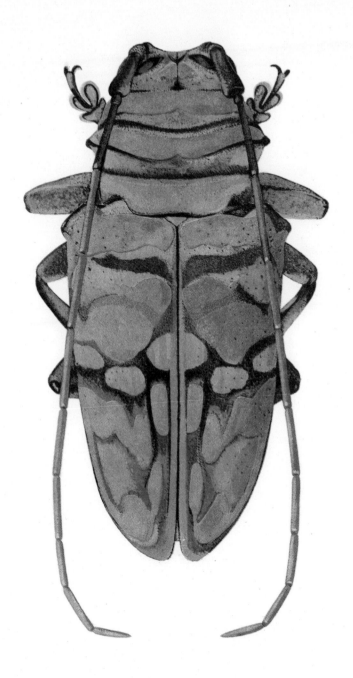

20 mm.

Rosalia alpina (L.)

___

Family *Cerambycidae*

The beauty for which the longicorns are famous is not confined to exotic tropical species, but is found also in beetles occurring in the temperate zone. As in most beetle families the tropical species show the greatest range of form and colour, yet the species from colder climates are not without interest. Certain species are able to withstand the cold climates of North America, central and northern Europe and the northern territories of the palaearctic region. The faunas of all these areas include a number of longicorns.

The legless, soft, white longicorn larvae resemble those of the *Buprestidae* both in appearance and in habits. As a rule they undergo their development under the bark or deeper in the wood of the trunks and branches of trees. They gnaw tunnels through the wood on which they feed. They are protected from extremes of temperature by the wooden walls of their tunnels. The rate of development is to some extent correlated with the temperature of the environment. In many cases the larval stage is extremely long. The larval stage of tropical species is often shorter than that of cold-climate species.

Rosalia alpina (L.) is a beautiful member of the family which may be found on bushes in central and southern Europe. The larvae live in old willows. This species has been introduced into the British Isles in beech. It is a beautiful blue-grey colour with a broad, transverse, velvety black band across the middle of the elytra and spots of the same colour on either side. The edges of the spots are somewhat lighter in colour, thus bringing out the contrast. The black pattern may differ a great deal from one specimen to another.

The antennae of *Rosalia alpina* (L.) are longer than the body. They are blue in colour and each segment bears a tuft of hair.

Although there are many attractive longicorns to be found in Europe *Rosalia alpina* (L.) is surely the most handsome of them all.

25 mm.

Leptinotarsa decemlineata (SAY)

Family *Chrysomelidae*

The Colorado Beetle, *Leptinotarsa decemlineata* (Say), which is sometimes referred to by the older generic name of *Doryphora*, is the most destructive member of this family. Originally its distribution was limited to Central and North America where closely related genera occur.

Before the introduction of intensive potato cultivation this species fed on wild solanaceous plants. In the first half of the nineteenth century it turned its attention to the potato and, multiplying at an increased rate, caused untold damage to potato fields in the state of Colorado — hence its name.

This species shows an unusual migratory habit which has led it to colonise new territories in search of food. There are references in the literature to an occasion when swarms of Colorado Beetles invaded the potato fields in a certain region of the United States and having ravaged them, flew on to the railway line. So great was their number that the oil from the crushed bodies made the line so slippery that the traffic had to be halted.

The effect of the natural tendency of this species to spread was increased by commercial shipping. It was introduced into Europe in 1870 and by 1877 it was a serious pest in German potato fields. Troop movements in two world wars helped to spread the species. Today the Colorado Beetle is found throughout the temperate zone whenever potatoes are cultivated. It has fortunately not become established in this country.

The Colorado Beetle occasionally attacks the foliage of the egg plant, *Lycium barborum*, tobacco and other related species, but the damage is slight, and in this connection the beetle is of little economic importance.

The adult beetle is orange or reddish in colour with fine longitudinal black lines on each elytron and a number of black patches on the thorax.

After mating the female lays her orange eggs on the undersides of leaves. After a few days the larvae, which are of the typical Chrysomelid type, hatch out. When they first hatch out the larvae are pink but later they become yellow with a black head and numerous black marks on each segment. The larval stage lasts about 3 weeks. During this period it feeds on potato leaves. It then burrows about 12 cm into the ground where it pupates. The adult beetle emerges in the autumn but remains underground throughout the winter. In spring it reappears and begins to feed on the young potato shoots.

Under favourable conditions there may be four generations in a single year. As a single female can produce 2,400 eggs an infestation soon reaches very serious proportions. There are fewer generations in cold regions.

It is very difficult to control this pest. Mechanical methods of catching and killing adults and larvae have been used. Dusting with D.D.T. powders and spraying with insecticides has proved successful.

The Colorado Beetle has been studied in great detail and there are many publications dealing with this pest.

8—10 mm.

Cassida murraea F.

Family *Cassididae*

The tortoise beetles (Cassididae) were formerly regarded as a subfamily of the leaf beetles (*Chrystomelidae*). Recent work has shown that they differ from the *Chrystomelidae* in a number of ways, and they are now treated as a related, though independent family.

The Cassidids are very interesting beetles and many species do in fact look very like little tortoises. The prothorax and elytra are convex and together form a 'shell' which may be so wide that only the tips of the tarsi show. In other species the 'shell' is narrower leaving the tips of the femora and the tibiae exposed.

Tortoise beetles live on and under plants. Many resemble the seed pods of plants; some tropical species even bear spines and hairs similar to those found on certain seed pods. If the beetle draws its feet in and becomes absolutely motionless it is very difficult if not impossible to detect it amongst the foliage.

In the Introduction, tortoise beetles were discussed in connection with pigments. Unlike most other beetles, many Cassidids change colour when they die. This is because the integument of the Cassidids contains pigment which decomposes when the beetle dies.

Some tropical species have a beautiful metallic colouration, but only as long as they are alive. This colouration is the combined result of pigment and refraction. The light rays are reflected by the pigmented layers and refracted by the chitinous integument above. When the pigment disappears there is nothing to reflect the light which simply passes through the integument. Cassidids contain more pigment than any other family and this is why they undergo greater colour changes when they die than any other beetles.

Members of the genus *Cassida* have characteristic spiky larvae which live in the top layers of the soil; they feed on plant roots.

Cassida murraea F. is found in the British Isles and is widespread in central Europe, though it is one of the rarer species of tortoise beetles. It changes colour very little after death. The elytra have an interesting and characteristic black pattern.

8 mm.

Hispella atra (L.)

Family *Hispidae*

The *Hispidae* have only recently been elevated to family rank. Before that they were regarded as a subfamily *(Hispinae)* of the leaf beetle family *Chrysomeloidea*. They are closely related to the leaf beetles and tortoise beetles. Together they form the superfamily *Chrysomeloidea*.

The Hispidae are found chiefly in the tropical regions. The fauna of South America, in particular, includes numerous brightly coloured interesting species. A smaller number of species occur in the temperate zone. *Hispella atra* (L.), illustrated here, is the only species recorded from central Europe. It is found only in very warm regions and does not occur at all in the British Isles.

The members of this family resemble hedgehogs. Their bodies are covered with close-set processes and spines. As the Hispids, like all other *Chrysomeloidea*, live and feed on plants, many of which bear spiky seed cases and fruits, these help to render the beetle inconspicuous amongst the plant litter. These seed pods vary greatly in colour, some are black and others yellow-brown or red — all colours found in the *Hispidae*.

Hispella atra (L.) is an inconspicuous species as regards colouring, but its shape more than makes up for this. Both the thorax and elytra bear sharp spines, and even the first two segments of the short compact antennae bear spines.

Hispella atra (L.) and other members of the *Hispidae* are good examples of a protective resemblance to the background against which they are seen.

3—5 mm.

Bruchus pisorum L.

Family *Bruchidae*

This family, though it contains relatively few species, includes some very serious pests. The small beetles which are often very attractive to look at, are often found on flowers.

The Bruchids are closely allied to the weevils, *(Curculionidae)* to which they bear a slight resemblance, and more distantly to the leaf beetles *(Chrysomelidae)*.

Certain species, amongst them *Bruchus pisorum* L., have become very serious pests. Originally this species, which feeds on peas, was probably restricted to Ethiopia or Iran but today it is found in all parts of the world.

The adult beetle is elongate-oval in shape with a transverse thorax and short elytra which leave part of the abdomen exposed. It is black with a slight sheen and the elytra are patterned with a multicoloured tomentose vestiture. The antennae are short and moniliform. The legs are short and stout with tarsi which are well adapted for climbing on plants.

The adult beetles may be found on flowering peas where they feed on pollen and copulate. After mating the female lays oval amber-coloured eggs which she attaches to the young pods by means of a glutinous secretion which hardens on coming in contact with the air. Eggs are sometimes laid on other parts of the plants, but not very often. At temperatures above 18°C the female lays an average of twelve eggs a day and may continue to do so for 47 days.

After about 9 days the fat, active Chrysomeloid larva (one resembling a leaf beetle larva) emerges. The larva has a peculiar spiny process on the pronotum which serves as a support when it bores its way into the pod. When the larva has entered the pod it works its way into a young pea. When it moults it loses its legs so that it resembles a fat Curculionid (weevil) larva. This process seems somewhat akin to hypermetamorphosis. The point of entry of the larva is marked by a small black patch. The larva eats its way to the centre of the pea, and in the course of its development consumes almost the whole contents. The larval stage lasts about 40 days during which time the larva passes through four stages. Before pupating the larva makes an exit hole about 2 mm. in diameter which it then seals. The yellowish-white pupa lies with its head towards the exit hole.

The adult beetle emerges after about 18 days and makes its way out through the exit hole. Frequently, however, the hole is too small and the beetle dies imprisoned within the pea. Some authorities believe that eating peas containing larvae or adults may be injurious to health.

Bruchus pisorum L. is monophagous, feeding only on peas; it does not attack any other leguminous plants. It causes a great deal of damage and may reduce the germination of a sample by as much as 75%. Control measures include the burning and ploughing in of infested plants and the use of chemical insecticides

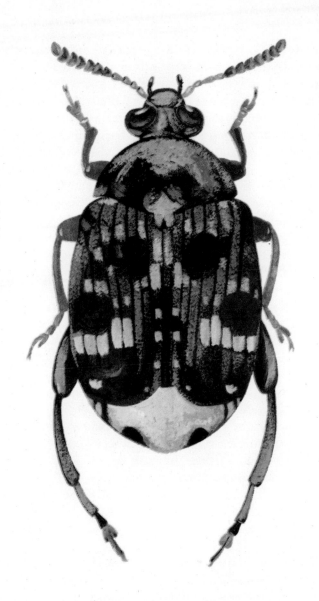

4—5 mm.

Zetophloeus pugionatus (CHEVR.)

Family *Brenthidae*

The members of this family are easily recognisable by their extremely elongate bodies. They look like very long weevils and indeed they have a number of characteristics in common with, and are probably closely related to this family.

The Brenthids are truly bizarre creatures. Some, like the East Indian *Calodromus mellyi* Guérin have fantastically shaped hind legs. In this species the tibia is short while the first tarsal segment is almost as long as the whole beetle in the male and a little shorter in the female. The inner end of this segment is thicker and bears projections with tufts of hair. The outer end has a finger-like projection with a tuft of hair at the tip. The use of this structure is unknown.

Another tropical species, the South American *Estenorrhinus designatus* Boh. has an exceptionally short wide rostrum with huge sharp mandibles. This too is a rare and unexplained phenomenon; the Brenthids usually have small mandibles almost entirely concealed by the rostrum. There are but two examples of the many varied and interesting characteristics displayed by the very diverse members of this family.

The *Brenthidae* are most abundant in the tropical regions of both the Old and the New World. In Europe they are confined to the Mediterranean region. Two species have been recorded from Italy, Yugoslavia, Greece, Crete and the South of France.

As their long slender shape suggests, these beetles are found under bark. The life history of some species, however, is closely linked to that of certain social insects, chiefly ants and termites, in whose nests they live.

The Madagascan *Zetophloeus pugionatus* (Chevr.), depicted here, is a typical member of the family and displays many of the characteristics peculiar to this family.

The narrow head bears an extremely long rostrum with a chisel-shaped tip which conceals the small mandibles. The eyes are very small and lie some distance from the mouthparts and antennae so that they are of use only for general orientation. It is evident from the structure and general shape of the body that these beetles move about slowly and probably live in dim, shady places. The structure of the antennae is of interest in that the last three segments are unusually long.

The thorax is comparatively long and narrow with a characteristic elongate furrow in the centre.

The elytra have several longitudinal ridges with large, regular pits lying between them, giving the surface the appearance of a regular lattice-work. The tips of the elytra are drawn out to form a long process whose significance is unknown.

This species is entirely black except for the shoulders where one rib has a longitudinal red mark and two others each bear a minute red dot. Elongate red marks are also present at the base of the apical processes.

Little work has been done on the Brenthids. The family has many puzzling structural features which have yet to be studied in detail.

55 mm.

Calandra granaria (L.)

Family *Curculionidae*

The grain weevil, despite its small size, is one of the most serious pests of stored foodstuffs. It has been recorded from wheat, maize, rice, buckwheat, chestnuts, dried beans and peas, soya beans and acorns. It is a curious fact that this insect finds cocoa beans, green coffee beans and certain seeds with a high oil content inedible.

The damage caused by this weevil is enormous. It has been shown that a single insect destroys about 25 seeds weighing about one gram in the course of its life cycle. The weevils not only destroy a great deal of any product they infest, but they also carry harmful micro-organisms such as moulds and fungi which are able to establish themselves on the damaged food material.

Calandra granaria (L.) was probably introduced into other parts of the world from the Orient. Today it is cosmopolitan. One week after copulating the female lays the ferti-lised eggs on the seeds. Using her mandibles she bores a shallow pit in which she lays the egg. The hole is sealed with a chitinous-gelatinous secretion which is the same colour as the seed and renders the hole invisible to the naked eye. Generally a single egg is laid in each seed, but 2—3 have been found in maize. The period of oviposition lasts about 200 days, the female laying an average of one egg a day. After 13 days the legless, white, brown-headed larva emerges and begins to feed on the contents of the seed. It consumes everything except the embryo and pericarp. The larval stage lasts about 63 days, during which time the larva moults four times. It then prepares a pupal cell in which it lies quiescent. Four days later it changes into the pupa which, though white in colour, resembles the adult with the legs, antennae and rostrum pressed close to the body. The adult beetle emerges after 9 days. The integument is at first light brown but it gradually darkens until the beetle is dark brown. The beetle undergoes its development inside the seed so that the damage it causes is not immediately apparent.

At a temperature of 18°C the whole cycle, from egg to adult beetle takes 98 days, but at the optimum temperature of 27°C the time is reduced to 35 days.

Calandra granaria (L.) is able to withstand extremes of temperature but it thrives best in places with a fairly high temperature and relative humidity. It is able to survive for 48 hours at 14°C and can remain under water without harm for 10 days. Adults often travel several miles in search of a suitable habitat. They are lucifugous insects, that is, they avoid light.

Many thousand pounds worth of damage is caused by *Calandra granaria* (L.). Infesta-tions are exterminated by physical means such as reducing the temperature and humidity and by treating the infested foodstuffs with chemicals. Because of its great importance as a pest of foodstuffs a great deal of literature on the problems connected with control of infestations has appeared.

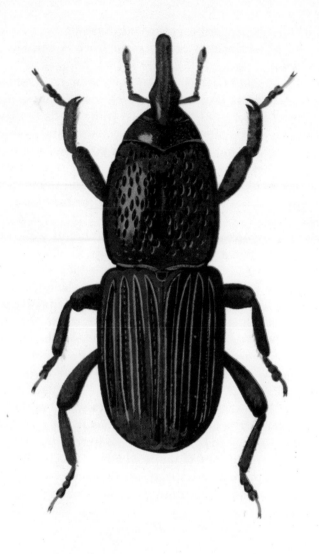

3—4 mm.

Paracentrocorynus nigricollis ROELOFS

Family *Curculionidae*

These weevils belong to a separate group, the *Rhynchitinae,* which are usually regarded as a subfamily of the *Curculionidae,* though some workers consider them to be a separate family, the *Attelabidae*.

They differ from the other *Curculionidae* by their straight antennae which are thickened at the ends and their short broad elytra which leave some of the abdominal segments exposed. This latter feature can be seen only if the beetle is viewed from the side.

The thorax and elytra are often attractively coloured and have a bright metallic sheen. They are usually glabrous, but a few species are pubescent.

The average length of these beetles is 10 mm. The rostrum varies greatly in size and shape from one species to another. It may be long and thin or short and broad as in the case of *Apoderus coryli* (L.). Some species have a forwardly-directed spine on each side of the prothorax.

The *Rhynchitinae* occur on willows, alters and birches as well as on vines and fruit trees where they frequently cause a great deal of damage.

These beetles roll up leaves to form funnels in which the eggs are laid. It has been mathematically shown that the curve of the funnel is always exactly the same, and is that best suited for the purpose. The action is entirely instinctive as the beetle has never witnessed the process before, nor been taught how to set about making such a funnel. This is another example of the importance of instinct in the life of an insect.

Cases of considerable modification of the prothorax are found among certain East Asian species of the *Rhynchitinae* such as *Paracentrocorynus nigricollis* Roelofs illustrated here. This species is a veritable giraffe amongst beetles. The black prothorax is very elongate, and the long narrow head is attached to it in such a way that it can be raised and lowered in a wide arc. Together the head and thorax look like a very long neck bearing mouth-parts and long antennae. The beetle appears to have a very long rostrum, but this is not the case. It is the posterior part of the head which is very elongate; the short rostrum begins just in front of the eyes which are set well forward. This species is rightly considered to be one of the most extraordinary species in the group.

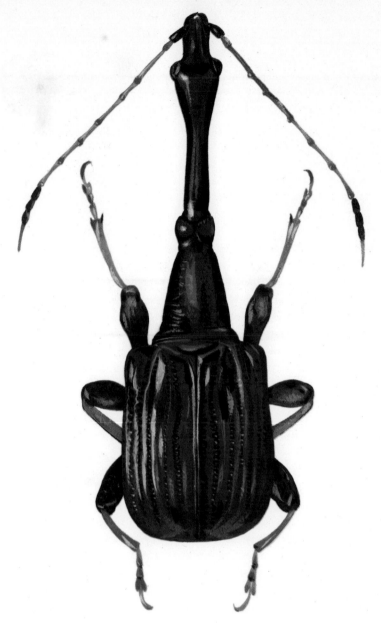

13 mm.

Ips typographus (L.)

Family *Scolytidae*

The bark beetles, *Scolytidae*, sometimes known as *Ipidae*, are of great economic importance for they do untold damage to forest trees.

The *Scolytidae* are small, cylindrical in shape, with four-segmented tarsi and antennae which terminate in a distinct, compact club. Many species bear characteristic tubercles at the tips of the elytra.

Members of this family are found throughout the world from the northern to the southern tree-line. The number of species of beetles is in direct proportion to the number of tree species, the greatest number occuring in the Euro-Asian, African and American continents. The Scolytid fauna of Australia, New Zealand and New Guinea is comparatively small. There are many harmless species but the family also includes a large number of extremely injurious beetles whose introduction and successful establishment may have disastrous consequences in forestry plantations. Because of its great economic importance, this family has been studied in great detail and much has been published on its life history and habits.

One of the most destructive and therefore most feared pests is *Ips typogrăphus* (L.) which has a very wide distribution. It is found in the British Isles and Scandinavia, throughout the whole of central and eastern Europe, and as far north and east as Siberia and Manchuria. It has also been recorded in Italy, Yugoslavia, Rumania and the Caucasus.

Ips typographus (L.) is confined almost entirely to pine but is sometimes found under the bark of other trees. It requires a thick cambium layer for its development and for this reason it attacks mainly full grown trees which are about 60 years old or even older. *Ips typographus* (L.) makes galleries in the wood under the bark and the layout of these galleries is characteristic of the species. The straight egg galleries run vertically up and down from the nuptial chamber which is made by the male in 2 to 4 days. The female, guided by her sense of smell, finds the entrance to the chamber, enters and mates with the male within. She then begins to gnaw the egg gallery in which she lays about 60 eggs at the rate of one or two eggs a day. She may copulate several times during this period.

The larvae resemble those of the *Curculionidae*, being stout and legless. They make galleries which lead away at right angles from the egg galleries. The larvae feed on the cambium layer and also on the mycilia of certain fungi which grow under bark. At the optimum temperature of 29°C the larval stage lasts 7-8 weeks. At the end of this time the larva pupates in a chamber it has made by widening the gallery. The pupal stage lasts about 14 days. The whole life cycle, from egg to adult, takes 6-10 weeks. The adult beetle remains under the bark until it has hardened and darkened. It then emerges and the whole cycle repeats itself.

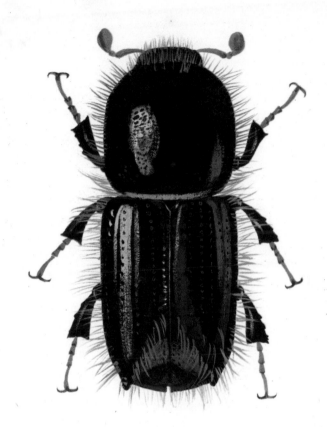

4.2—5.5 mm.

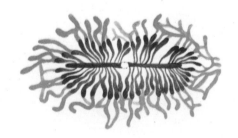

INDEX